THE
MA

THE MANSE

MEREDITH RESCE

Authentic
LIFESTYLE

First published in 1997 by Golden Grain Publishing
PO Box 93, O'Halloran Hill, SA 5158, Australia
This edition published 2004 by Authentic Lifestyle

10 09 08 07 06 05 04   7 6 5 4 3 2 1

Authentic Lifestyle is an imprint of Authentic Media,
9 Holdom Avenue, Bletchley, Milton Keynes, Bucks,
MK1 1QR, UK and
PO Box 1047, Waynesboro GA 30830-2047, USA

British Library Cataloguing in Publication Data

A catalogue record for this book is available from the British
Library

1-86024-444-0

Cover design by Daniel Chattaway
Print Management by Adare Carwin
Printed and Bound in Denmark by Nørhaven Paperback

To the Australian 'Green Valley' readers

Your enthusiastic response has proved to me that these
stories will be loved the world over.

ABOUT THE AUTHOR

Meredith Resce was born and raised in the Southern Flinders Ranges of South Australia, in the community of Melrose.

Meredith and her husband Nick have worked in the ministry for eighteen years, having served a six year period in Geelong, Victoria. They now work with Southside Christian Church in Reynella, South Australia.

Meredith has completed a Bible College Certificate Course and also a certificate course in psychology. Apart from writing, Meredith Resce lectures to groups on various subjects including development of relationship skills and growth toward emotional health.

She has three teenage children, Elisa, David and Michael.

ACKNOWLEDGEMENTS

Thanks to all those who have helped in the shaping of this book from the very beginning, and to Malcolm Down and Sheila Jacobs who've been instrumental in getting *The Manse* ready for the international readers.

Thanks Phil Baker for being the vital link between Authentic Media and 'Green Valley'.

Thanks to my family, particularly my grandmother (101 this year) and mother who are the biggest 'Green Valley' fans. Elisa, David and Michael: thank you for embracing the whole idea of romantic fiction, even though it's probably not your style.

My husband, Nick: romantic fiction is not really your style either, but you believe in me so much that you're my best promoter. Thank you.

Thanks must go to Simon Malcolm of SM Media, Dan Chattaway of X-Media, David Scarallo, Lauren Beaty, Caleb Cure, Lisa Roper, Rosina Coppola, Jill Young and Bronwyn Dansie who all helped to get the new cover ready.

Most of all, thank you to my Lord Jesus Christ who is the author and perfector of my faith.

CHAPTER 1

Melbourne, Australia 1880

John Laslett gazed around the drawing room, allowing his attention to fall on the table laden with cakes and sandwiches. His appetite failed as he realised again why his mother had thrown this lavish afternoon tea.

'Ah! Here he is! The new minister himself.'

John cringed inside as he heard his mother's voice all but command his attention.

'John, my darling,' she went on, oblivious to his discomfiture, 'you'll want to meet our guest of honour. Reverend Thatcher, this is my newly ordained son, John Edward Laslett.'

'Pleased to meet you, Reverend.' John shook the man's hand without conviction.

'Well, John Edward Laslett,' the rotund man's voice boomed across the gathering.

'You may call me John.' Without allowing him to continue, John made this expectation clear.

Not at all ruffled, Reverend Thatcher continued. 'Your mother informs me that you are looking for a parish to begin your work.'

'My mother has misinformed you, sir.' John spoke a little too hastily. 'I have already been offered, and have accepted an appointment.'

'Oh! Pshaw!' Mrs Laslett overrode the comment easily. 'My boy means well in accepting the position, but it is of no account. Only a small congregation way out beyond civilisation. The bishop really didn't expect him to take it!'

'Indeed!' The reverend gentleman raised his eyebrows in surprise.

'I for one intend to speak with the bishop, and have him reconsider a placement for our boy in one of the Melbourne city churches.'

Without so much as a 'by-your-leave', John left the conversation, hardly caring if his departure seemed rude. His mother's overwhelming interference was so stifling it almost choked him. Though he found a quiet corner of the room, he was unable to find the peace he sought. He knew it would only be minutes before she would summons him again, probably this time to fling him at the Reverend Thatcher's daughter, Bernice.

'You'll need a wife who is brought up to the position!' He recalled his mother's words of the day before. 'Bernice Thatcher will be just the woman for you . . . Oh! And don't worry that she's three years older than you, dear. She is mature and ready for marriage straight away!'

John shuddered at the thought. He'd not yet met the young lady in question, but he had seen her. At first he'd been afraid that she would be less than attractive. Considering her age, and not yet spoken for who could have blamed such a doubt. But when John saw her, he knew immediately why she'd not yet married.

Bernice was a beautiful young woman, but domineered completely by her father. Obviously, the Reverend Thatcher had been hard to please in his search for a suitable son-in-law. John was not necessarily pleased to realise that the Reverend Thatcher evidently deemed him, John Laslett, to be the first appropriate marriage candidate for his daughter. Bernice showed her lack of confidence in the way she conducted herself. She never so much as lifted her eyes from looking at the carpet; she never spoke beyond the polite 'how-do-you-do', and almost had to wait to be told what to eat from the large choice of food laid out.

'It would be good if you could discuss engagement plans with the reverend.' John was snapped out of his reverie by his mother's piercing whisper that was a poorly disguised attempt to be discreet. 'He's expecting you to approach him about it today.'

Despite the feelings of indignation that instantly rose up, John nodded mutely.

'Oh! And if you would only ask him, I know he will put in a good word for you with the bishop!'

Before John had used the chance to protest, his mother had swished away, instantly taking up conversation with another well-to-do couple.

You've got to make up your mind, John! He spoke to himself. *After all, Bernice is rather beautiful to look at. You could be well set up here in Melbourne. Mother has a lot of influence to exert. You only have to walk over to the Reverend Thatcher, propose to his daughter, ask for a relocation and you'll have everything you could ever need.*

John didn't stop to think how his slapping his side in frustration might look to those standing nearby. *Everything I could ever need*, he thought angrily, *but nothing of what I desire!*

With that thought, John moved forward, armed with the motivation to do what he knew he must do. For the first time in his twenty-four years, he was going to defy his mother.

Green Valley – Rural Victoria, Australia

Kate wiped the soft dusting cloth over the oak bookcase for the third time in an hour. Even though the rest of the house was in dire need of a good dusting, she felt closer to her father by just being in his office. She ran her fingers over the gold embossing on the leather volumes, mentally reading each title as she touched it. Finally, as she saw the precious letters of The Holy Bible, she crumpled before the bookcase, tears spilling from between squeezed lids.

Her father's absence was supposed to be temporary. She knew he'd gone to her mother's funeral – the mother who'd deserted them both when she was no more than a year old; the mother she'd never known, and would now never know. He had left the manse only four weeks ago, and had assured his daughter it would be best if she stayed behind. Kate had not worried overly much at the time, being as she expected her reverend father to return within the week. But instead, to her shock the ordeal had just begun. 'How could they treat him like this?' she asked herself yet again.

She thought of the nameless 'they', who'd coldly informed her that her father was officially relieved of his duties at the parish. 'A disgrace', she recalled the words used to describe the most loving and caring man she'd ever known. And where was he now? Taken ill, and housed by the only charity hospice in Melbourne. And she, his only family, without finance or means to go to him.

The tears continued to flow as she mourned, not just for her mother, but more for the loss of her father's life work. The labour of love he'd sown into the humble people of Green Valley Parish.

She did not know how long she would have remained in the bowed-over stance of sorrow, had she not been drawn by a knock at the front door.

Bravely, Kate drew back the cedar portal, wiping quickly at a stray tear.

'Good morning, Mr Hodges,' she smiled at the waiting gentleman.

'Excuse me, Miss Winston,' he tipped his hat politely, if not a little nervously. 'I . . . ah . . . I've been sent to inform you that you are to be out of the house by this afternoon.'

At first, Kate was speechless, sure that she hadn't heard the man correctly. 'I beg your pardon?'

'You're to have your personal effects packed and out of the manse by one o'clock at the latest. I'm sorry Miss Winston!'

As if the message was too hard for him to deliver, Mr Hodges turned on his heel, ready to depart.

'But I can't possibly have packed all my fathers books by then. And what of the furniture?'

'Just your own clothing, Miss Winston. Everything else is part and parcel of the manse.'

'But it all belongs to my father – the minister!'

'Beggin' your pardon, Miss, but there is a new minister set to arrive at week's end, and Lady Vera wants the manse ready for cleanin' out unwanted rubbish. I'm sorry, Katie.' He used the less formal name he was used to. 'That's the message I'm supposed to have delivered to you!'

Kate watched helplessly as Hodges made good his intentions and left. She stood staring at his departing figure until he was a long way down the drive, and may have stayed watching longer if the cold hadn't driven her back indoors. It took some time for her mind to begin to function again, and when it did, despair crowded in to mock the previous sorrow.

She had no money. She had no close family to turn to. Already she'd felt the cold stares of the parishioners, and she knew that they had already labelled her as part of her father's so-called misdemeanour. She looked helplessly around the manse, at every beloved nook and cranny. This house was the only home she'd ever known. It was in the master bedroom that she had been born, a little over nineteen years ago, delivered by the wife of a local farmer.

The grandfather clock in the hall struck eleven o'clock, as if to remind her that she had but two hours to rearrange her entire life – she had two hours, and nothing more. What was a little time when she had nothing else? She knew that Lady Vera would have her people in to pull the house apart by two minutes past one. Lady Vera's reputation was well established, and though Kate's father had often excused her harsh, self-righteous actions as the pride of the privileged, Kate knew that that pride would act without thought or feeling for anyone, much less the daughter of Reverend Winston, whose scandalous behaviour had so offended the pious lady.

But what was she to do to save her father's sermons, and some of the bric-a-brac he'd held dear? Where on earth was she going to store them, to save them from the impersonal sorting that was due?

There is no other choice, she whispered to herself. *I have to move now or I'll lose everything*.

Before the handsome clock had time to strike the first hour, Kate Winston had removed as much personal memorabilia as she was able, and carted it across the church yard. Having taken the iron key from beneath the doorstep flagstone, she opened the door into the church vestry. There, beneath the desk, she lovingly placed her father's things. It would have to do until she made room in the store shed. If she worked hard enough, she could have cleared away the broken pews, hidden the treasure, and made herself a dwelling, before night fell.

She shivered at the thought. If only she'd had time to gather a blanket. But wasn't it bad enough already? She was already suffering from the effects of her father's deception, being looked upon as if perhaps she was a liar too. It would not do to be accused of being a thief as well. Her winter overcoat was going to have to do.

The emotional storm was over, but John could still hear the sound of angry accusation reverberating in his mind. Having stood his ground thus far, he was encouraged to go forward as planned, despite the incensed ravings his mother had cast in his direction. He could still see her face as it changed from one of determined scorn, to shocked outrage.

'John Laslett,' she had spoken in authority. 'I will not have you speaking to your mother with such disrespect.'

And later, as it became obvious to her that he didn't mean to relent, she continued. 'What of me? Have you ever thought of anyone but yourself? Who is going to take care of me, now that your father is gone, God rest his soul?'

'You have two other children, Mother, remember. Sandra and her husband are here all the time, and Pauline is only an hour's drive across town.'

'You expect me to put my life into the hands of complete strangers! What is Sandra's husband to me? This would never happen if your father were still alive. He would have demanded you respect my wishes!'

John recalled his hen-pecked father, who'd resigned himself to the voicing of his wife's commands and decrees, every time she ordered him to. He thought also of his two brothers-in-law, both of whom stood up to the pompous Mrs Laslett. John knew that both of them thought him to be a spineless creature, unable to think or do for himself. Now that the subject had been brought up, he was suddenly determined to make a stand for himself.

'And have you thought what a burden this will be for Bernice? Her father is not going to want her to be galli-vanting off to Lord knows where – to a place where he is unable to handle her affairs.'

'Bernice and I have already spoken, and we've decided that the time is not right to be considering a hasty mar-riage.'

At this point, Reverend Thatcher, who'd been monitor-ing the heated exchange, burst forth in his own indigna-tion. 'What do you mean you've been talking with my daughter? Neither of you have the right to be making any decisions whatever concerning Bernice. It is outright impudence, and I won't have it!'

John remembered casting a quick glance in Bernice's direction, and seeing her trembling with fear. His heart melted with compassion again and he wondered if he might not have at least rescued her from the tyranny she lived under. But his mind just as quickly recovered. Marrying Bernice would not rescue her from tyranny, more than it would place them both under double the control they now experienced.

'I won't listen to you, John. I will go to the bishop this very afternoon and demand he give you a respectable position.'

'Green Valley Parish is quite respectable, I assure you. The Lady Vera Wallace is the patron, and she has already sent directions about my expected arrival. This is my decision, Mother. This is the choice I have made for my own life!'

Indignation had crumbled quickly into an emotional tantrum, where the respected lady of Laslett House had fainted completely away, and the doctor had had to be summoned. With as much dignity as possible, John dismissed the remaining guests, knowing full well that the entire exchange had been heard by all. When he had seen the reverend and his daughter to the door, he had cast Bernice a sorrowful glance. He hoped that he had been successful in communicating his regret at having left her stranded. He knew that he had not been the only one to hear her father's boasting of an impending engagement. Reverend Thatcher walked out without so much as a nod of his proud head.

Now, in the quietness of his own room, John fought off the guilt that threatened to overwhelm him. *I have done the right thing. I will go to Green Valley, and I will serve the parish as properly as the bishop himself.*

Lady Vera Wallace had sent word that she expected the Reverend John Laslett to take residence of the manse by the 23rd May, and that his first sermon would be delivered the following Sunday. John felt a thrill of excitement at the prospect. In two days time, he would take the train the eighty miles to Brinsford, and travel the last twenty miles in Lady Wallace's private carriage, to Green Valley Manse. From the 23rd May, John Edward Laslett would be his own man, free to make his own life's choices, without his mother's interference.

Kate awoke with a start as she heard voices approaching the shed. At first she froze, instantly realising that she could well be discovered in her new hiding spot. She listened to the sounds outside the shed, and was soon satisfied that her hiding place was not threatened. Quietly she began to rub the aches, developed from lying on a hard wooden pew.

'We'll build a bonfire just here,' she heard a man suggest.

'Right! You go inside for some more rubbish, and I'll hunt around for some decent kindling.'

Kate strained to hear more, but it was obvious there were only two, and that they had gone about the proposed business. Racked with curiosity, Kate hunted for a way to be able to see what was going on. It crossed her mind that a fire might actually provide some warmth for her, which would be better than shivering in the already cold autumn weather.

It didn't take too long for her to discover a small hole in the side wall, left there after a large nail had been, for some reason, extracted. Shifting a few things around, she made herself relatively comfortable, and waited for the men to return.

But the curiosity, that had so motivated her, quickly turned to horror as she saw one of Lady Vera's employees carrying an armload of things toward the proposed bonfire site. Her first impulse was to cry out, but her need for secrecy prevented it just in time. Still she crumbled on the inside as she saw her very own bed quilt, being dragged out to be burned.

'Dear Lord! Why didn't I think to bring it with me?' She mourned. This was no ordinary quilt that could have been passed on to the new residents. This quilt had been pieced together, by hand, and had her own name and birth date embroidered as a centre feature. Her grandmother Winston, who'd been the only mother she'd known, since her own had left, had proudly talked of this quilt. She'd boasted how her little Kate would have this quilt for the rest of her life, and when she married . . .

Kate bit back another cry of anguish at the thought. This precious quilt had been stored away in a chest in the attic, waiting the time when she could use it for her own marriage bed. Grandmother Winston had died when she was only seven, but she'd left her granddaughter this and other personally embroidered household items. These were to be as a dowry – a gift for the future from beyond the grave.

'Why? Why?' Kate cried out silently, angry at what she saw through her tiny viewing place.

It crossed her mind to race out of the shed and grab up the quilt from the growing pile of 'rubbish', but she knew that she must not be discovered trespassing on Lady Vera's property. Lady Vera was well known for her callous and relentless upholding of the law. Hadn't she called the troopers to arrest a family who'd camped on her property? She hadn't listened to Kate's father's plea on their behalf. To her, it was against the law, and no matter what extenuating circumstances, the law was to be upheld. Prosecuting a trespasser was nothing but an afternoon's job well done.

'Perhaps I can rescue it from the flames after the men leave?'

Kate watched with renewed hope, all but willing the two men to return indoors. But it soon became apparent that they intended to use their job to warm their hands before going about other tasks.

Tears of frustration and despair welled and flowed down her cheeks as she watched the greedy, orange flames gobble up that last piece of comfort. Not only could that quilt have kept her warm in the draughty shed, but also it was her last connection with the grandmother she had loved so dearly.

There and then, Kate allowed a seed of bitterness to be planted in her once soft heart. 'Reverend Laslett, whoever you are, I loathe you for coming and taking everything from me.'

⚜

The journey from Melbourne to Green Valley had been uneventful, in that no physical mishaps had arisen to impair an otherwise smooth passage. But John's mental state was a little less than free of mishaps. From the moment the great steam engine had pulled away from the Flinders Street Station, till the time he alighted at Brinsford, his emotions churned with second thoughts.

'Have I made the right decision? Will Mother be all right?' Flashing scenes of his final departure came forward as if to haunt him. He could clearly visualise his mother as she refused to farewell her son. He saw her stubborn, angry look, even as she had tried to turn her face from him. It was these disturbing memories that kept encroaching upon his sound mind. Her words of final pleading echoed in his memory. 'I shall die without you. At my funeral, you will know that you are responsible!'

John shook his head as if to free himself from the troubling thoughts. 'It is too late anyway,' he lectured himself. 'My responsibility is to Lady Wallace now.'

For the moment, he felt free to enjoy the passing countryside. It was only then that he realised how beautiful the open land was, away from the crowded, noisy streets. God's beautiful creation found no suitable comparison to the pomp and ceremony found in his mother's world. Breaking from the virgin scrub that often enclosed the countryside, John now noticed the rolling green hills, lit with the afternoon sun; the few gum trees left after

clearing marking out splashes of contrast; even the graz-
ing sheep dotted over the hillsides, all spoke of a peace
and tranquillity not found in his former place of residence. John inhaled a deep breath of the fresh, crisp air,
and found a sense of contentment.

'I will write to Mother tomorrow. She will learn to live
without me. She will be all right!'

The light had almost merged with the darkness by the
time Kate woke from her fretful sleep. The temperature
had dropped alarmingly, and Kate shivered, pulling her
Sunday coat closer around her quivering shoulders.

That this tiny storage shed was now her home was a
fact that she had at last come to accept. She had walked
the whole day from farm to farm, and finally into the
small township of Green Valley, but had come away
disappointed and discouraged. It wasn't that the humble farming folk wouldn't have welcomed her in
instantly: more that she didn't have the courage to ask.
Several times it was on the tip of her tongue to pour out
her whole distressing story, but each time she swallowed the tale, and forced a smile. These people loved
her – of that she had no doubt. These were the people
for whom her father had laboured for years and years;
the poor and struggling families who welcomed his
prayers along with his efforts to aid them through the
harsh economic times. Yet none of these families ever
set foot inside the grand Green Valley church. Those
bluestone walls had been constructed in memory of the
late Lord Wallace, by his loving wife, and she intended
to see that only 'respectable' people ever crossed the
threshold.

Reverend Winston knew the farming community was made up of hard-working, respectable people, but he was never able to convince them that they would ever be welcomed into his Sunday congregation. The oft-quoted excuse was they could never greet the patron lady without being properly dressed, and they simply didn't have the means to obtain the required items of clothing. So Kate's father had ridden from home to home, delivering the Word of God, and brotherly love. He understood their 'pride' and never condemned them for it.

Even as this scattered congregation didn't have the means to buy the decent Sunday dress, Kate was aware that they could ill afford another mouth to feed – for she had no money or skill to bring with her in return for board.

Eventually, Kate, after having visited nearly every single family, returned to Green Valley. She had come to the end of her options, with only the general store left, but the hope of finding help here was remote. The small weatherboard building was situated just across the road from the church, and she calculated the risk of being seen there after having been evicted from the manse. With the desperate need foremost in her mind, Kate decided to go forward and at least see if there was any possibility of help.

'Hello, Miss Winston.' Kate smiled weakly at the lady behind the counter. She knew that her greeting was born of common courtesy and not from any personal affection. She knew there would never be any sense in seeking a place to stay here. The Booths, owners and proprietors of the general store, fancied themselves one cut above the ordinary folks of Green Valley, and their fierce loyalty to Lady Wallace motivated their every action.

'I see you have not left the Valley,' Mrs Booth made the pointed remark. 'I daresay Lady Wallace expects you to have gone by now.'

Kate chose to ignore the comment, not having any sensible explanation to offer. She pretended to browse through the shelves, trying to formulate a plan of action. Even after a quick prayer, she was still without inspiration. She was almost at the point of giving up altogether, and confessing her plight to the harsh judging Booths, when her eyes lit upon a small hand-printed notice, hanging in the front window.

*A situation is vacant for the position of housekeeper/cook
for the Reverend Laslett.
The applicant will need to be able to start immediately,
must have references,
and have their own accommodation.
Please address your application to Lady Wallace.*

'So! Reverend Laslett needs a housekeeper,' Kate whispered under her breath, anger already evident in her tone. 'I daresay I know of someone who could keep the manse tolerably well!'

Carefully removing the notice from the window, Kate walked out of the store, renewed vigour in her step.

CHAPTER 2

John felt a shiver of excitement as his eyes fell upon the bluestone sacred building – the Green Valley Church. He hardly heard the detailed history that Mr Hodges carefully recited for his benefit. All that he could think was that he had, at last, found a place and calling that were his alone to command.

Lady Vera Wallace had earlier offered the proper, gracious welcome, extending her bejewelled hand for John to bow over. He had allowed the thought to cross his mind that his mother would most certainly approve of the genteel Lady Vera. And as she continued to issue her directions as to his proper conduct, and a decree of what she wanted to hear preached as a sermon the next Sunday, John wondered if she might not have been his mother in another form. But he quickly dismissed his misgivings as Hodges drove him away from the magnificent Wallace residence toward his own humble dwellings.

'Lady Vera'll arrange for a housekeeper,' Hodges' gruff voice broke the atmosphere. 'My wife, Mrs Hodges, will see to your needs 'til then!'

John acknowledged the statement with a nod, having not ever considered the domestic workings of a household before.

'That'll be your place over yonder!'

John's gaze followed the direction of Hodges' finger, and once again, felt equal thrill at seeing a home of his own. He took a deep breath of the twilight air, exhilarated by the adventure of finding a new life.

'Tell me, Mr Hodges. Should I expect this wonderful feeling every time I come home for the night?'

The burly driver chuckled under his breath. 'I should say the feelin'll wear off soon enough,' he ventured, 'less you can find yourself a good wife, o' course. That's a different story!'

Kate stiffened with a variety of unwelcome feelings as she heard the carriage pull up to the manse. 'So you have arrived, Reverend Laslett!' Her assumption was that this replacement must know why he was called, and already, bitterness laced her mumbling. 'You have come to gloat over my father's demise, no doubt, and to take from him every last ounce of dignity! Well! We shall see how well you do.'

She peered fearlessly through her convenient peep-hole, and watched as Hodges opened the carriage door for 'his grace'. Kate was all prepared to unleash the building resentment upon a proud, overweight personage, but she was somewhat cut off in her poisonous murmuring. She found herself taking a quick gasp as the sight of the new minister took her unawares. At first, when she saw the face of a young, innocent boy reflected in the carriage lantern, she looked further to get sight of the objectionable reverend; but when Hodges opened the gate and urged the young man to follow, addressing him as Reverend Laslett, she was completely defused.

It took her almost a whole night of tossing and turning to rekindle the flames of bitterness.

'But he's so young,' she kept arguing with herself. 'He looks so innocent.'

But just as she was about to give in to an unidentifiable emotion – something akin to warmth – she would quickly regroup. 'But it is because of him that I am here in this shed, with nothing, and my father . . .' She would allow the thought to trail off in all of its evil insinuations.

John took yet another deep breath of appreciation. He looked with anticipation across the room to the ornate bookcase, full of theological commentaries and doctrinal expositions. He felt full. Full of purpose; full of hope; full of provision. Lady Vera had seen to everything. The manse may not have been his mother's home, but it had everything in it he needed for the immediate future, and he could not help but feel the satisfaction of the moment.

A knock at the front door shook him from his reflective mood, and he pulled himself out of the leather desk chair. Mrs Hodges had already left for the day, and he felt no trouble at having to answer his own door, though he made mental note that he would not mention that in his letter to his mother.

Outwardly, Kate stood as confidently as if she were the Queen of England. Inwardly, she shook like a leaf in a furious storm. She doubted her resolve only a moment, but knew her course was set when the door – the front door that was so familiar as her own – opened up to her.

'Can I help you?' A pleasant smile lighted John Laslett's handsome face, and brightened just noticeably when he saw the lovely young woman standing on the doorstep.

Kate felt as if her heart might yet stop. A furious conflict of emotions battled within – resentment and resolve fought with the softer part of her that wanted to forgive this man who could not have known what he had done.

'I . . .' She faltered for only a moment. 'I have come to keep house.' She held back the desire to exhale.

John's smile deepened yet again, as he stepped back to allow Kate passage into her own home.

'Lady Vera has been so good to me. She has seen to every detail.'

Kate heard the gratitude in his tone, but withheld open comment. *Lady Vera has taken everything from me*! The thoughts came easily, now.

<hr />

Kate washed up the dishes – the very plates and cups that had been hers only days before – and tried not to give in to the urge to smash every last one on the flagstone floor. She had cooked the young minister's breakfast, served it to him, and stood back, trying to appear busy; hoping that he wouldn't notice the look of hunger that she felt must be evident. Her stomach had twisted painfully as she had smelled the sizzling bacon, but she refused to give in even to this most basic desire. It wasn't until John had asked for a second cup of tea to wash his toast down with, that he'd apparently noticed she was even there. Up until then, he'd been deeply engrossed in a book he'd found in the mahogany bookcase – *one of my father's books* – Kate had thought angrily.

'Why don't you pour yourself a cup,' John had kindly offered, as she placed the pot back on the table. 'You must have been up early, and it's been a while since you've had breakfast, I daresay.'

Kate had been sorely tempted to tell him that she'd not eaten since her visit with a local family yesterday, when they'd politely offered her a slice of bread with a cup of weak tea. But she had nothing if she didn't have her pride, and it was with this pride that she struggled. Eventually, she forced herself to accept the tea. It was with great difficulty that she spoke the thoughts that had been tumbling around in her mind ever since she'd first announced her intentions to take this job.

'I hope you won't think me rude,' she began, her voice lacking warmth, 'but I wonder if you would mind my eating breakfast after I've finished cleaning up yours each morning.' She didn't wait even for a breath before continuing. 'I had difficulty managing breakfast before getting away for work.' The statement was quite truthful, despite withholding the full story. She didn't bother to elaborate that the difficulty was in her having no food, fire or plates. She paused – half ashamed, half afraid he would detect the truth. It was hard waiting for his answer with her eyes cast down and away from his gaze.

'Of course I don't mind!' John watched Kate carefully, hoping to establish eye contact, and wondering what it was that had created such a barrier between them from the very first. But even with his full attention focused on her, he could not draw any more from her. He watched closely for a short time more, until he realised that she was not going to respond, or allow him to get any closer. He broke his attention, and had no sooner done so, than she finished drinking her tea and quickly stood up to continue with her chores. John was baffled and intrigued at the same time, and determined in his mind to break through the hardness that so obviously existed.

Kate remembered all that had happened over the breakfast table, and flushed with the embarrassment of having had to actually ask. It went quite against her grain to do so. She sighed as she hung up the tea towel, and attacked the bench top with a frustrated vigour, wiping the crumbs away, almost as if she could wipe away her regrets.

John left Kate at her kitchen duties, dwelling only a moment on the thoughts that had been buzzing around in his mind since she'd introduced herself the evening before. But to spend time thinking on how beautiful a young woman his housekeeper was, would certainly not have fitted into the criteria of a dedicated man of God. Certain that it would be an expectation to take control of his thoughts he reluctantly pushed these sentiments aside. He was about to step into the study when knocking at the front door, not two steps away, arrested him. For the second time in as many days, he stepped forward to answer his own caller.

'It's all right,' he called back to Kate in the kitchen. 'I will get the door.'

He didn't have time to finish the thought of what his mother would have judged at him opening his own door, as he was caught unawares by the caller herself.

'Mrs Hodges!' He allowed a friendly smile, though he couldn't hide his surprise.

The dumpy woman's face told of her confusion. 'I'm sorry I'm late,' she spoke uncertainly. 'My husband would have come to make apologies, but it was the horse that made us late in the first place. Went lame!'

'Late for . . . work?' John guessed, somewhat confused himself.

'O' course!' She seemed a bit put out. 'Less o' course you got company. Wouldn't want to be disturbin' you none!'

'Oh, no!' John hurried on. 'It's just that Lady Wallace has already sent a permanent housekeeper.'

'Oh?' Mrs Hodges seemed curious. 'She didn't tell my man nothin' 'bout it.'

'I'm sorry,' John apologised. 'It must have been a mix up.'

'Who'd she end up sendin' ya?' The older woman didn't try to hide her prying.

'A Miss Oliver. Kathryn Oliver.'

'Never heard of her!' Mrs Hodges tone spoke her lack of approval. 'S'pose she'll do the job all right!'

'I'm sure she will.' John tried not to sound too enthusiastic, but he was sure that he preferred the company of the young woman, wounded in spirit though she may be, to the gruff and forthright Mrs Hodges.

Kate remained well hidden, holding her breath as she heard the exchange at the front door. She didn't want the people at the big house to know she was still in the Valley. That was why she had used her mother's maiden name, and not her real name, Kate Winston.

⁂

Kate allowed a half smile to express her feelings. She felt pleased with the way things had gone for her. She didn't know the full extent of the story, or she would, perhaps, have offered a prayer of thanks to God for the way one piece fell in with another.

She did not know that Lady Vera Wallace was still under the assumption that Mrs Hodges was working as housekeeper at the manse. It had not occurred to Kate how it was that everything had strangely worked out for her. She did not know that the Lady had almost forgotten about the notice she had posted in the store window – the notice that was no longer there to advertise for a permanent girl. Lady Wallace had left the matter in the hands of her manager, requesting that she be informed the moment an applicant came forward. She had also ordered that an extra something be put in Hodges pay to make up for his wife's extra duties. Neither Kate nor the Lady knew that Hodges never looked in his pay, which he always handed straight to his wife. Nobody was aware that Mrs Hodges had accepted the extra coins as a pay rise for her husband's efforts. Nothing was said, and nobody asked. Kate remained in the manse, employed by no one, paid by no one, but happy and secure nonetheless.

It had taken some thought, but Kate had managed to organise things in such a way that she would not be seen by anyone save the minister himself. She gave a small chuckle at the idea of the Reverend John Laslett living under the notion that his housekeeper came early each morning and left each night for her own home. She knew he believed that Lady Vera saw to her pay, and that he gave no thought to her affairs whatsoever. The truth, of course, was a far cry from what John Laslett had been led to believe. Kate did in fact appear each morning, but she had come no farther than from the back room, once her own bedroom. She would make an early detour, via the church store shed before coming to work, and back there again in the late afternoon, before sneaking in to her own warm bed as soon as the minister had retired for the night.

Kate had suffered only a moment's guilt at the thought of the minister's food she had been consuming, but quickly brushed it aside as she justified her actions. *I work very hard for what I eat*, she reasoned. *A little food and board is the least I can expect*!

It was only the second day at her new post before she realised she would be expected to stock the pantry. At first she had paled at the thought of boldly arriving at the grocers and the butchers, and the questions that would be asked that must lead to the discovery of her deception. But then her clever mind had devised a neat plan. It had been easy enough to get John Laslett to give her the amount of money she thought she would require. He didn't seem at all concerned with the affairs of running a home. It was the second part of her plan that took some work to effect.

Sitting at the humble table of the Browning family, Mrs Browning, motherly in her welcome and consequent concern for the young girl, caused a few moments of worry.

'I don't know if your dear father would approve of what you are doing, Kate,' she offered gently. 'I'm sure, even in the circumstances, it is not good to be lying, especially to the minister himself!'

'Mrs Browning, I have no choice!' Kate moaned. 'Where on earth could I go? I have no money. God knows that!'

'You had only to ask, dear, and we would have welcomed you here!'

Kate knew the truth of it, but as her eyes scanned the room and took in the twelve young occupants who all sat on the crude, wooden planks, politely watching their visitor, she knew what she would say. 'I thank you, Mrs Browning, I really do, but you and Mr Browning have enough responsibility with your own brood without taking in another mouth to feed!'

'Nonetheless, we would do it, and do it happily!'

Kate smiled again, and toyed with the idea for just a moment. But she saw the patched and worn clothes the children wore. She saw the hospitality offered, knowing it was the best this woman had to offer. It may have been only a crust of bread and a smattering of butter, but Kate knew that it was extended with generosity and love. And with the same kind of love, Kate knew that she could not take food from the mouths of these children, no matter if she had to lie.

'Please, Mrs Browning,' she continued with her original request. 'If your Pete could do this job for me, I will make sure he gets a penny each time.'

'But Kate . . .'

'All he will have to do is to come to me for the shopping list, take it to the shop, and bring back the groceries.' Kate continued to promote her idea.

'But he will have to lie for you!' There was no mistaking the concern in the mother's tone.

'He need only tell the shopkeeper that it is for the housekeeper at the manse. There is no need to be using names. Besides, Kathryn is my real name, and Oliver is my mother's maiden name, if he gets in such a corner he needs to use a name at all!'

'I'd be happy to help Kate, Mama.' The eldest child, a fourteen-year-old boy offered his support. 'Imagine the money I could save up!'

'Please!' Kate added her best tone, sure that this good-hearted woman would help her.

Mrs Browning hesitated, obviously weighing up the wisdom of the decision in her mind. A dozen pairs of intense eyes stared hopefully at her, adding pressure to her initial convictions. At last she could take it no more. 'All right!' She released the words. 'But only on the condition that the minister knows you are paying Pete to be an errand boy. He must know, or I will not allow Pete to come. Agreed?'

'Agreed!' Kate said the words without thinking, and it was only later that she dreaded having to go back to her employer to ask, once again, for something.

But if she thought that John Laslett would put up any form of protest, she would have been mistaken.

'Is that all you need, Miss Oliver.' John seemed content to oblige any request that his housekeeper put to him. 'Is there anything else I can do that will make the job easier for you?'

If Kate could have seen inside his heart, she would have been surprised to see a deep care for her growing steadily each day. No, John was not falling in love, or at least, he didn't think so. But John was challenged to the point of worry. He was concerned not knowing quite what kept Kate at such an emotional distance – her sullen silence, and haunted eyes. There was much that John saw that bothered him. He was determined to break through the wall of bitterness that surrounded her, justifying his decision with thoughts of pastoral motivation. He would not allow any other inspiration an audience in his mind.

'I didn't see you in church on Sunday!' He stated in an off-handed manner one morning.

'I wasn't there!' Kate's answer was short and detached.

'But you must go to church, Kathryn. Everybody does!'

'Do they?' She kept her eyes on the pile of dirt she was sweeping, and refused to indulge in the conversation.

'I hope you will come next week. I would love to see you there!'

'Not everybody is welcome in that church!' She spat the last word, unable to hide the bitterness in her tone.

'Of course they are. Everybody is welcome in the body of Christ!' John recited in his best clergyman's voice of authority and care.

'That shows you just how much you know, Reverend.' Kate was merciless in her condemnation. 'If you opened your eyes, and looked beyond the walls of the Wallace estate, you would see a whole community of people who worship God – but not at church. They worship him at home because they are not welcomed by her Ladyship!'

John was truly surprised by the accusation that Kate had thrown at him, and did not feel equal to the task. That her words were true, he did not doubt. But to actually think on them and do something about it was something that he had not been taught in seminary, and so he hurried away, and attempted to forget the incident by burying himself in his study. 'What an odd thing to say,' he muttered, one moment before he allowed his attention to be absorbed by the huge commentary before him. 'Of course everybody is welcome in Green Valley Church. Lady Wallace is a most generous benefactor!' It was difficult, but John managed to push the disquieting thoughts aside, and restore his comfortable belief in the good nature of the grand Lady.

Sometimes, at night, when Kate was curled up in her own warm bed, she argued with herself. Essentially, she was a compassionate and forgiving personality. The many times she had worked with her father, serving and ministering to the poor and humble folk of Green Valley had only fostered these traits. Now she seemed to have reached the point that she found she was at war with her own nature. The bitterness and resentment that burned with passion each time she thought of her father's and her own cruel eviction, seemed almost to peter out as the contrasting spirit appeared, intent on resurfacing. The temptation to give in and return the youthful minister's smile was at times overwhelming; and stronger yet was the lure of conversation with him. John Laslett had exerted himself in a mammoth effort to break down the communication barrier by gently asking questions, paying compliments, and generally being pleasant in spite of her hard, cold responses.

But in all of her night-time musing she seemed able to find at least one thought that could rekindle the flame of resentment she so desperately wanted to keep alive. If it were only the memory of his inability or unwillingness to take up the cause of the needy families, it was enough. Kate was disgusted by his apathy. She would not allow herself to make excuses for him in this matter. Lady Wallace was proud and arrogant, and had elevated herself to the position of being the one who chose those who were fit to worship in her church, and those who weren't. If it were only Lady Wallace, Kate could have perhaps softened her attitude. But she saw the same attitude reproduced before her in the new minister. No matter how handsome and how attentive he was to her, the Reverend Laslett allowed himself to be dictated to and ruled over by this higher influence. It all went against what Kate believed to be good and right. It all went against what her father had taught her, and when she came back to this point in her thoughts, the bitterness was renewed all over again. In it all – the remembering, the justifying her anger – Kate failed to see the seed of sin in her own heart. She failed to recognise the destructive power of resentment and bitterness, and so she let them burn.

The routine at the manse had fallen into a happy rhythm – at least, John told himself that it was happy. He held hope that he would soon break through to his housekeeper, and be able to find a kind heart and soft nature. Kate kept the house efficiently, and could never be accused of being late. The fact that she actually lived on the property went unnoticed by the head of the house.

There was never so much as a suspicion; in fact, the thought never crossed his mind. He believed Miss Kathryn Oliver to be a God-sent gift to lighten his thoughts.

The only thing that John did wonder about, though were the strange noises he heard in the night – every night – not long after he'd turned down the lamp. He had been tempted to get up to investigate at first, but the chill of the night had deterred him. He had decided that he would wait to see what, if anything, would eventuate. When no intruder burst into the house, and no flames leapt in the hallway, he eventually fell asleep, easily dismissing the noises.

When they occurred the second time, he thought on it again, but then explained it away as normal country noises. *Probably wild cats or foxes*, he thought to himself.

Night after night the same noises echoed in the dark, and each day revealed that nothing had been damaged or stolen. *At least I am not actually being burgled*, he comforted himself. But this thought led to others that were less easy. Perhaps he should never have read the cheap thriller novels that had captured his imagination in his youth. Even with this new resolve, the ideas had still been sown in his mind, and the damage done. After weeks of listening to the strange sounds, John was finding it more and more difficult to convince himself that the manse was not, in fact, haunted. If he had gone to investigate the first night, when he'd thought it was a cat, it would have been easy enough, but now that his imagination had conjured up all sorts of ghostly images – ideas he couldn't erase – nothing could entice him from his bed. John Laslett went to sleep each night praying that God would deliver his home from the demonic intruders.

Kate had no idea that her nightly entrance back into the house was even being heard. She would perhaps have laughed outright if she had any idea what her employer was troubled with. Still, she would never enlighten him as to the real source of his fears. As far as she was concerned, she came and went in secret, and so she would remain in Green Valley.

CHAPTER 3

~~~~~~~~~~~~~~~~~~~~~~~~~~~

Winter had been raging its bad temper for nearly three months now, and the folks of Green Valley watched the calendar in anticipation of the day that spring would arrive. But despite the collective wish for warmer weather, it appeared that the cold season had a particularly cruel purpose, and was intent upon saving its worst burst of fury until last.

With the plummeting temperatures came the cutting winds, and Kate shivered under her only coat, uttering a prayer of half-hearted thanks that she was at least not still living in the store shed.

Kate didn't complain at all to him, but she had noticed that John was rather absent-minded when it came to the chores about the house that belonged specifically to him. Occasionally, the wood-box was full, as it was supposed to be, and Kate had no particular difficulty in stoking and maintaining the cook stove or the other fireplaces in the house. But just as often, if not more so, it appeared that John would simply forget that it was his own responsibility to see to the fuel. Instead of openly reminding the minister, Kate would go about the chore herself, using his neglect of responsibility as a reason to mutter her discontent to the woodpile.

Her own ill-temper and strong willed determination kept her out in this unusually harsh weather, swinging an axe wildly in an attempt to complete the job. The icy rain dampened her hair and her coat, and if it weren't for the warmth gained by the exercise, she would probably have frozen.

By the time the job was finished, Kate was all but soaked through, her temper at boiling point. But she was triumphant that she had not had to beg the reverend for anything at all.

'At least I can dry out in front of a warm fire,' she murmured to herself.

'Kathryn!' John captured her attention the moment she walked through the door with an armload of the newly cut wood. 'Thank goodness! I thought you'd already gone home for the day.'

'I never go home until after I have cleaned up from your dinner!' Kate retorted, none too pleased, and even more annoyed that he had not noticed her doing his job.

'No! Of course not!' He brushed the idea aside, and went on just as quickly. 'Do you think you could prepare some afternoon tea quickly? Hodges has just sent word that we should expect Lady Vera within the hour.'

John was so caught up in his own moment of glory – the idea of entertaining someone of class – that he completely failed to notice the blood drain from Kate's face. He hurried out of the kitchen intent upon the impending visit, and left his housekeeper in a state of agitation.

Eventually, Kate dumped the load of wood in the wood-box, and automatically took off the soaked overcoat. 'I haven't got any time to stand about getting dry now,' she muttered to herself. 'I'll have to get something on a tea tray and get out of this house before she gets here!' There was definite bitterness in her tone as she brushed over the reference to Lady Wallace. With hair still wet and her clothes damp, Kate hurried about the small kitchen, mixing a batch of biscuits, and cutting some small sandwiches.

It took the best part of an hour, and the biscuits were still warm when she arranged them on the plate, but she at least had something to offer. She left the kettle simmering on the back of the stove, and left a note on the silver tea tray.

I am sorry to have had to rush out, but I've had word that my help is needed straight away. Everything is ready. Just pour the water into the teapot.

The note was short and lacking in any real apology, but it was all she could think of in such a moment of tension. Kate had just put the tray on the kitchen table when she heard the rap on the front door. She had no intentions of opening the door, but rather that she would be far from the house by the time the dominant woman put her foot over the threshold.

With this in mind, Kate took up her wet coat, knowing that she had no time to go into her room for anything dry, and she fled into the cold and blustery afternoon. She paused at the corner of the house and watched as Hodges assisted Lady Wallace from her covered carriage, carefully holding an umbrella above her grey head. Once the visitors had obviously moved inside, Kate broke away from the side of the house, more wet now than she had been when cutting the wood, and headed toward the store shed.

'How long will she stay?' Kate asked herself, worry now beginning to climb in her voice. 'I have to get out of these wet things soon!'

'Lady Vera!' John expressed his welcome as best he could, considering that he was forced to open his own front door, yet again. 'This is poor weather to be paying a visit. I do hope nothing is wrong!'

An icy wind blew through the door as he spoke, as if to accentuate his remark; and with it, Lady Vera Wallace also seemed to blow through. John felt her cool sense of aloofness.

'If you had sent word with Mr Hodges, I would have been pleased to come to the house to see you.' He tried to establish some form of confidence.

'Never mind that!' Lady Vera snapped. 'There was no time to delay. Let me come straight to the point, Reverend Laslett.'

John shivered under her intensity.

'A serious matter has been brought to my attention and I'm here to get an explanation immediately!'

'What is the worry?' John asked, instantly intimidated.

'Hodges tells me that his woman has *not* been keeping house for you!' The older woman glared at John, as if he should know instantly what she was getting at. She paused for a meaningful moment, obviously expecting him to break down and confess.

'I'm sorry, Lady Wallace,' he stammered. 'I'm afraid I don't quite know what the problem is.'

'Well! Has she been keeping house for you, or is my man telling the truth?'

'No! Of course not! I thought Mrs Hodges . . .'

'Don't tell me you are one of these radical people who believes in doing for himself!' She rudely cut him off. 'I won't have it, Reverend. You occupy a respectable position in this community, and you will conduct yourself as a gentleman. Do you understand?'

'I beg your pardon,' John was only slightly relieved, but more so confused. 'I was under the impression that you sent Miss Oliver to serve as housekeeper. She has been working here since the day after I moved in.'

'Miss Oliver?' Lady Vera raised her eyebrows in a disapproving glare. 'Who, sir, are you talking about?'

'She told me that you had employed her to keep house here at the manse.' Now John was not just confused, but a little afraid that Kathryn had put herself in a precarious position.

'Send for this woman!' Lady Vera snapped. 'I will speak to her myself!'

John got up from the sofa, instantly alert to the tension of the situation.

'Where are you going?' The proud woman's arresting voice caused John to pause. 'Surely you have a bell. Ring for the woman!'

Reluctantly, John moved to the bell cord and rang. Ordinarily, he would not have had a problem with this, in his former home, but with Kathryn, he had so much wanted to make her feel at ease. Perhaps it was a vain hope that she might one day confide in him. Nevertheless, John rang as he would for any nameless servant. After all, Lady Wallace had ordered him to, so there was little choice in the matter.

After a few tense minutes of waiting, John was further agitated by the fact that Kathryn had not responded, and he resolved that he would have to speak to her on this issue. 'My apologies!' He bowed slightly to his guest before continuing. 'She must be otherwise engaged. I will go and have her fetch afternoon tea in for you.'

'Never mind the tea! You must speak firmly to her. This lack of cooperation is certainly not to be tolerated in an employee.'

John moved out of the drawing room, his nervousness at an all time high. Lady Vera was not a woman to be arguing with, but then, neither was Kathryn Oliver a character easily confronted on any issue. 'Miss Oliver!' His tone was in fact quite apprehensive, and he called several times before he saw the tea tray and the note, telling of her hasty departure.

'Well! I'm beginning to doubt your word, Reverend Laslett,' Lady Vera spoke haughtily. 'Does this Miss Oliver indeed exist, or is she just a convenient excuse for an otherwise unorthodox habit of doing for yourself?'

'I am sorry,' John apologised again, as he poured tea into a china cup. 'I had no idea that things were not as they seemed. When the young lady turned up at the door and announced that she was here to fill the position, I assumed that all the details had been seen to by you.'

'Young lady, you say?' Her tone was suddenly accusing.

'Miss Oliver would not be far into her twenties, I would guess.' John sounded defensive.

'I don't like this situation at all! How much have you been paying her?'

'Paying her?' John sounded alarmed. 'Why, nothing. Only the grocery money. I mean to say, I was under the impression that you had made the arrangements, and she had been employed by yourself.'

'I daresay.' Lady Vera sounded amused. 'You realise that Mr and Mrs Hodges have been enjoying a housekeeper's earnings all this time, thinking of it as a raise in Hodges' pay.'

'Well, who has been paying . . .? I don't understand what has been happening here at all!'

'Where does this young woman live, Reverend, if I might be so bold as to ask?'

'Live? Why I don't . . .'

'What do you know about her, other than the fact that she has a pretty face?'

John reddened at the remark. It was a fact he could not deny having noticed, many times.

'I see we shall have to wait for her to return before getting any answers. When do you expect her?'

'She didn't indicate,' John began, still defensive. 'She will be back soon, I should say. She has always been here to cook dinner.'

'Then there is nothing to do but to wait, is that not so?'

Kate had been in the store shed for the best part of two hours. She had checked to see if Lady Wallace's carriage had gone, perhaps a dozen times, but to her dismay, the horse stood sadly, dripping wet, in the front drive way. Kate may have spared a sympathetic thought for the horse had her own plight not been so desperate.

There was nothing, no clothes or blankets, in the store shed to help keep her warm, not since she had taken all her belongings back to store them safely in her room in the manse. But now, Kate all but cursed herself for not having left something out for such an emergency as this. She had taken off her drenched coat, and even some of her other damp outer clothing, but if she thought that they would dry in the freezing damp air, she was sadly disappointed. She didn't know whether it was better to shiver with the little clothing, or take some form of comfort from extra clothing that was wet.

Stamping her feet constantly on the earthen floor, she hoped upon hope that the next time she peeked outside she would see the front yard clear of any signs of visitors. But to her dismay, the situation had not changed, and in fact, did not change until the daylight was all but gone. Kate knew that the dinner hour was upon her, if not past, and that John would be wondering why on earth she had not fulfilled her normal duty.

Finally, her ears told her that the carriage was pulling away from the manse. Though relieved for that much, Kate was still panicked. She knew the signs too well not to be worried. Already her bones ached, and though the temperature in the shed had not changed, she felt hot and feverish.

'What else can I do?' she asked herself as she began to move back to the manse. 'There is nowhere else I can go!'

John finished eating his meagre dinner. He wanted to be angry with Kathryn, but there was too much anxiety about what he had learned to allow his annoyance full reign. The fact that he had been forced to fix his own evening meal – which ended up nothing more substantial than bread and jam with tea – was not the most upsetting thing for him to consider. Who exactly was Miss Kathryn Oliver? And more importantly, where had she come from, and what was she doing here? These questions and more were enough to completely distract the minister from his domestic discomforts. John was so tangled up with his musings, that he did not notice the very person who featured in them, peering in the small kitchen window.

Kate shivered violently, still damp and standing in the biting wind, and definitely in the grips of a fever. Her aching body insisted that she throw caution aside and seek the warmth of the cook stove, but her logic still held enough power to keep her standing in the freezing night air, trying to formulate a plan. She knew she would not be able to sneak in through the front door, as that had a dead bolt. The back door into the kitchen was her only option, and was currently hampered by the fact that John was taking his time at the tea table.

Eventually, Kate was driven to the point of taking a risk. It took all of her strength and concentration to let herself in the back porch, without letting the wind snatch the door from her grip. She reeled with dizziness over and over, but was determined she must move quietly. Taking her shoes off, Kate set her gaze on the doorway that led from the kitchen. She would liked to have watched her employer's back, just to make sure he didn't turn around, but she knew she would most certainly lose her balance if she did not keep her eyes forward, as she moved.

Perhaps it was the howling wind, or crackling fire, or maybe it was just his own intense train of thought, but John neither heard, nor sensed Kate's presence back inside the manse. Kate might have offered a prayer of thanks, but her energy was spent. She had only enough will power left to change from her wet clothes, allowing them to fall to the floor in an untidy heap. Despite the thick flannel night-gown, and the feather down quilt, Kate was gripped with spasms of shivering. Her teeth chattered mercilessly, and she slipped further and further from the realms of consciousness, and into the depths of delirium.

John was forced from his position at the table as he realised that the kitchen fire had died down to mere embers. His mental dilemma had been such that he had completely lost track of time, and it wasn't until the chill of night began to invade the house that he knew he would have to either go about the business of stoking the fires or retire for the night. He opted for the latter, not having any motivation to sit up studying. There was little room in his

thoughts for anything save the current mystery surrounding his housekeeper.

For a change, John didn't wait to turn the lamp down.
On many occasions over the past evenings, he had waited, not at all willing to admit fear of his imagination, but
making all sorts of excuses as to why he needed to keep
the lamp bright. He was well aware that the night-time
manifestations would not begin until the house was in
complete darkness. Every other night he had waited until
tiredness was upon him, and hoped he would not hear
the noises he had now begun to believe was a ghostly vis-
itation. Yet every night was the same. Soon after the lamp
was out, he would hear what he thought were footsteps
in the back part of the house.

Tonight, however, his own worry was enough, without
the thought of a supposed ghost. He had been lying in
the darkness for nearly an hour before he realised there
had been no noises.

Perhaps my prayers have been answered, he thought to
himself. With this new hope, John was determined to get
a good night's sleep. But as much as fear had been dealt
with for the night, his anxiety was determined to take its
place, and John found himself tossing and turning, the
many questions taunting him, demanding answers he
simply couldn't give.

It was nearly two in the morning before John was able
to slip into a fitful slumber. His mind would not allow
him the luxury of deep sleep. And so when the footsteps
began again, echoing in the night, he was instantly pulled
from his precious sleep. Though the wind still whistled
and howled outside his window, John knew that the noises were back to haunt him. The storm outside only added
to the terror that seemed all too real to him. John shuffled
through his memory, trying to find a suitable prayer that

would fit such a situation as this, but came up sadly lacking. For a brief moment, he wondered if God would mind him speaking his own thoughts, instead of those penned by his superiors.

Unlike other nights, the footsteps seemed to be drawing closer to him, and the closer they came, the easier the decision became. 'God help me!' There was no more time for elaborate wording. The prayer would have to do. But despite his sincerity, the ghost came closer, until John was sure it was in his own room. For the first time in his entire life, John had to admit he was paralysed with fear. He wanted to reach over for the matches, to light the room, but he was unable to move, and so stared into the inky darkness, hoping that he would be able to see the monster that was every moment getting nearer.

It was not until the last second before the covers were pulled back from his tense body, that John realised that he didn't have a plan. There was nothing he could do to escape a supernatural attack. There was nothing to do, but submit to it. John felt the 'thing' get into his bed, and even heard it breathe. But when he felt a warm, slimy hand reach out in the darkness, and touch his face, he could contain his terror no more and he let out a yell, finally leaping from his bed.

'Papa! Papa! Please don't be angry with me. I'm so cold!'

John's terror melted away in an instant. He fumbled for the matches, immediately determined to establish the truth. By the time the lamp's glow dispelled the darkness, his emotions had taken a huge leap from the grips of fear to utter amazement.

'Kathryn!' He exclaimed. 'What on earth are you doing here?'

John paused, obviously waiting for a sensible explanation but the woman who lay curled up in his bed, though he knew her, appeared to be altogether different. It was only as she spoke again that he understood that something was dramatically wrong.

'Papa!' Her voice was as pathetic as a small pleading child. 'Please hold me. I'm so cold.'

John stared in disbelief as she held out her arms toward him, apparently delirious and believing that he was her father.

'Kathryn! What is the matter with you?' He asked the question, but somehow didn't expect an answer.

'Please!' Kate's tone was reduced to a tearful plea, and John, already being close, couldn't hold back any longer. He sat back down on his bed, and reached out to gather her close. As she snuggled close into his embrace, he was instantly aware that he held a very sick woman, whoever she may be. He could feel the burning of her body even through the thick nightdress, and now that he looked more closely, could see that her hair was drenched with sweat.

'Kathryn Oliver, if that's who you really are,' he began in a comforting tone, 'here you are, dangerously ill, and I don't even know where to begin to help you!'

CHAPTER 4

It had been a desperate few hours. John had seen this situation once before, and he recognised the gravity of the circumstances.

Once, when he was only twelve years old, his older sister, Sandra, had been taken ill with a fever, not unlike the one that now gripped Kathryn. Of course, his nanny had ordered him away from the sick room. He had been warned to keep well away from that part of the house, but several things had caused him to disobey that warning. One thing was that he was left without a companion. His mother rarely took an interest in any of her children. They had been left to the care of a nanny, and it was her job to see to their entertainment. The second reason John had disobeyed the order was that he sensed the worry and fear in his nanny's voice, and he began to be afraid for his sister. He had not been informed of any reason why he should not go into Sandra's room, but he discerned that all was not well. He had quietly slipped into the sick room, and stood behind the efficient nurse. He watched as she worked to bring the fever down.

'Will Sandra be all right?' John remembered the question he'd eventually asked his nanny. The gifted employee had not railed and scolded her second charge, but rather answered carefully.

'Your sister is very ill, John, but if we pray, and work to keep this fever down, I think she will live.'

Sandra did live, of course, and John didn't know it then, but he had been given a valuable lesson in how to nurse a fever. A lesson that he now remembered and put into practice.

With all the care and tenderness he had witnessed in his nanny's actions, John sponged Kathryn's burning face and arms. He did not allow her to overheat under too many blankets, and tried with great patience to make her take sips of cool water.

All the time, John found himself praying. The many disapprovals of his senior colleagues, as to whether he should use his own words in prayer or not, were cast aside. John asked the God whom he served to restore health to Kathryn. It was that simple. The many other considerations of the day before had been dropped in the order of importance. John did not even think for a moment as to who she was, or even what she was doing in the manse.

By the time dawn lightened the sky, Kathryn had settled from her state of agitated delirium, to a restful position. It seemed to John that the fever had broken, but he was not sure, and wanted to get a more expert opinion. The daylight revealed that the storm was still intent on raging, but regardless, John resolved to get extra help.

It did not occur to him for an instant what someone else might think about the situation as it was in the manse. All he could think of was getting someone who could help nurse Kathryn back to health.

Because Hodges had offered to stable his horse up at the great house, due to the cruel weather, John had only his own legs to carry him. Bracing himself against the cold and the rain he set out to deliver the message to Mrs Hodges. He took the best part of an hour to walk through the mud and wind, and finally delivered the news to an astonished Mrs Hodges.

Silently, Hodges hooked up a covered buggy to take the pair back to the manse. Neither man nor woman said anything to the minister. The many questions would be asked – had to be asked – but for the moment, the emergency was the foremost concern.

'Will she be all right, Mrs Hodges?' John's concern was evident in his tone.

'She's very sick, sir, but with God's help, I'd say there'd be every chance she'll be restored to us.'

'Thank God!' John breathed his sigh of relief.

Mrs Hodges pottered aimlessly about the small kitchen for a few moments, apparently trying to gain nerve to speak her mind.

'Go on, woman,' Hodges growled. 'I know you've a piece to say. Let's have it.'

'And you don't?' She threw an accusing glare at her husband. 'You don't mean to be tellin' me this situation is not a wee bit alarmin' to ye?'

John looked anxiously from one to the other. 'What is the problem, Mrs Hodges?' he encouraged her to speak.

'I have ta say I'm surprised at ye, sir.' She sounded harsh. 'To think you'd impose upon the good graces of her Ladyship, and in such an immoral manner.'

John looked from one to the other, an inkling of what they had assumed beginning to dawn on him. 'It doesn't look good,' he began, 'but it is certainly not what you are thinking.'

'What, sir, are we supposed to be thinkin'?' The large woman was obviously unconvinced. 'We're called to the manse at the crack o' dawn to find an unmarried woman, in her nightdress, in your bed, no less!'

'Please, I am as surprised as you!' John sounded desperate. 'Believe me. When she first wandered into my room, last night, I was dumbfounded.'

'It's a pretty sort o' story to be tellin' us, and that's for sure,' Mrs Hodges continued, 'but I'm findin' it mighty hard to be acceptin'.'

'It is the truth.' John cast a pleading glance toward the stern, yet silent husband. 'Miss Oliver disappeared from the house yesterday afternoon, and didn't return to prepare the evening meal. I went to bed about ten o'clock. I didn't sleep well. Lady Wallace had been to see me yesterday afternoon. I suppose you must know about the mix up that has occurred with Miss Oliver.'

'If you're talkin' 'bout that young woman who's in your bed, that'll not be a Miss Oliver.' Mrs Hodges didn't sound amused at all.

'Do you mean to say that you know her?'

'Tell him!' She flung the command to her husband. John turned his attention in that direction as well, in hopes of finding an answer to the question that had plagued him most of the night.

'The young lady be Katie Winston. She'll be the Reverend Carlton Winston's daughter.' Hodges revealed the news gruffly.

'Carlton Winston?' John sounded confused.

'He'll be the minister who occupied your position before he was disgraced.' Mrs Hodges sounded self-satisfied, as if she had delivered her point quite clearly.

'I'm afraid I don't quite understand.' John sounded genuinely troubled.

'Lady Wallace had him removed from his privileged place of influence because of his moral misconduct. It'd appear she might need to be doin' the same for you, young man. I have to say, I'm mighty disappointed in both of you. Katie always appeared a good sweet girl, but I suppose with her father bein' the deceiver he was, it was only to be expected.'

'There has been no moral misconduct, Mrs Hodges. I must make that quite clear. All I have done is try to save a woman's life. That cannot be a sin.'

'Now, young fella,' Hodges finally interrupted, 'we'll be getting to the bottom of this, and that's for sure. Lady Wallace will want a full and complete explanation. Just as soon as young Katie is well enough, we will hear her side of the story. For the time being, we'll take you at your word.' He glared meaningfully at his wife. 'There won't be any need to be upsettin' the good Lady 'til we know the full story.'

John walked on eggshells for the next few days. He didn't dare venture near his own room, not to retrieve his own personal effects, nor to inquire after the patient; not for any reason at all. He did not want to appear attached in any way shape or form to the young lady, despite the fact that his heart ached for her. He waited patiently for Mr Hodges to reveal her condition, without asking after her.

It had become clear to the three of them that Kate Winston had indeed been a resident at the manse for the past months. John felt embarrassed to think that all of his night-time horrors had, in fact, only been his housekeeper settling herself for the night. He felt compassion, when he understood that she had been forced from her home, with nowhere to go, and no one to turn to. Still, in light of Lady Vera's fierce determination to uphold social and moral appearances, John could not afford the luxury of following his feelings. He remained aloof and detached from all to do with the former minister's daughter.

'So! You've been telling us the truth!' Mrs Hodges conceded one afternoon, as she emerged from the sick room.

John thought she appeared disappointed that he was innocent.

'Has Miss Winston spoken? Is she out of her coma?' Despite his best efforts, John was unable to hide the anxiety in his tone.

'She has, sir!'

'And?' John was suddenly impatient for answers.

'And she's cleared you of all wrong doing, though I doubt that Lady Wallace'll see it that way.'

'Now, then, Mother!' Her husband rose uncharacteristically to oppose her opinion. 'Young Katie had no choice. We all know that. And the young minister here was completely unaware of what was going on. I don't think we need to be upsettin' the good Lady with all that unnecessary detail.'

'I'm sure Lady Wallace is well aware we been focusin' our attention down here at the manse these past few days.' Mrs Hodges was not appeased. 'She must know somethin's amiss by now.'

'Lady Vera's under the impression someone at the manse is ill. I didn't tell her who. She'll assume it's the reverend. She knows you're back doin' the housekeepin'. She wanted ta know 'bout the mysterious Miss Oliver o' course, but I felt best we not tell her 'til Katie's safely back with her father.'

'So, you know where her father is? You can send Miss Winston to him.' John sounded hopeful.

'T'isn't quite that easy, I'm afraid. We know where he was when he took ill in Melbourne. I daresay we can track him down from there.'

'So you'll see to it that Miss Winston is gotten to him.'

'Not exactly!' Hodges spoke slowly. 'I was kind of hopin' you'd see your way clear to help us. Lady Wallace hasn't been exactly benevolent toward young Katie, ya see. She probably wouldn't take kindly to our takin' her in like.'

'Is she really that arrogant?'

'Now, you best be choosin' your words carefully, son,' Hodges warned. 'I'm not here to be makin' judgements on my employer. For the time bein', it's enough that we see Katie safely to Melbourne.'

It was barely eight days since Kate had taken ill, and she was being escorted from the manse and tucked into a covered buggy. She wanted to thank Mrs Hodges for her care and concern, though she wasn't sure that it may not have been a little forced. She struggled to keep herself upright as dizziness assailed her constantly. Mrs Hodges had announced that she would be strong enough to travel, and she had not wanted to argue. It had not been easy knowing that her scheme had been found out, and to know what it was that she had done in the middle of the night. She had not seen John at all while she was sick, and felt he must be absolutely disgusted with her behaviour toward him, but there was little she could do to retrieve the situation. She was simply too ill, and even with health, she had little defence with which to justify herself.

'Mr Hodges'll see you safely to Brinsford, Katie,' Mrs Hodges had informed her. 'He'll see to it that you're put on the right train to Melbourne.'

Kate wanted to cry out her fear. *I don't think I can even hold myself upright, let alone find my father in a strange city.* But her lack of strength stayed her argument and she went along with the direction the Hodges had planned for her. She did not have any energy left to mourn her departure from the manse. At least all her

personal things had been packed and moved out with
her.

By the time Hodges had pulled the horses up to the
railway station, Kate was completely drained. All she
wanted to do was crawl back into a warm bed.

'Mr Hodges, I'm sorry!' Tears brimmed in her eyes. 'I
can't go on. I don't know if I can even stand up. I just can't
do it.'

Mr Hodges patted her arm in a comforting way. 'You
just wait there a moment, Katie. Things'll be all right in
the end. You'll see.'

She watched him walk away from the hitching rail,
after he'd tied the horses, and shook her head mournfully. *I just can't do it!* She sighed under her breath.

John saw Hodges coming towards him on the platform.
'Have you got the tickets, son?' Hodges asked the moment
he saw the minister. 'Yes! It's all arranged. Are you sure that
Lady Wallace understands my trip to Melbourne?'

'She's allowed you a trip home, considerin' your recent
illness. She hopes the rest'll do you good.'

'I'm not really happy with her believing a lie.' John
sounded troubled.

'You can correct the misunderstandin' when you
return. By that time she'll be knowin' all about Miss
Oliver.'

'How is she? Miss Winston, I mean?'

'Not really well enough to travel. If it hadn't been so
necessary, I wouldn't have brought her away yet. You'll
need to get her some medical care as soon as you can.'

John nodded his understanding. The pair walked
toward the buggy. Hodges spoke to Kate first.

'Reverend Laslett'll help you find your father, Katie.'

Kate looked every bit as horrified as she felt, but she
had no energy to formulate an argument. 'It'll be all right.

He knows where to find your father. By tomorrow, you'll be safely back with him.'

Hodges nodded his head toward the trunk, indicating that John should bring it to the train. He then turned back to Kate and urged her to let him help her down.

'I feel so frail, Mr Hodges,' Kate apologised. 'How ever will I make it?'

'Just you do your best, and we'll see to whatever else needs doin'.'

Reluctantly, but with no other choice, Kate leaned heavily on her old friend's arm. He guided her carefully and slowly to the train carriage, almost lifting her aboard, and eventually settling her in a seat. 'Send us word when you're settled, Katie,' he asked kindly. 'And please pass our regards on to your father.'

Kate nodded weakly. Hodges patted her gently on the shoulder before moving out of the carriage. Kate let two warm tears spill from her eyes. She had no motivation to wipe them away.

John saw the emotion she displayed, and suddenly felt helpless, left as the guardian of someone he didn't know how to handle. With a great deal of trepidation, John stepped forward and took his seat next to her. Taking a deep breath for courage, he decided to come straight to the point.

'I am so sorry that things have worked out the way they have for you, Kate.' He used her proper first name for the first time. She showed no emotion at his words. 'I didn't know how things were for you. You must have hated me for taking over your home like that, and for taking your father's place. I didn't know. I am sorry.'

Kate couldn't hold back the full extent of emotion then. Carelessly, she allowed the tears to stream down her cheeks. It was all too much. And now she was uncertain about her future.

John noticed and felt compassion. Without fuss or ceremony, he helped her to remove her hat, placing it carefully aside. Then he gently leaned closer, and placed his arm around her shoulder, allowing her to cry, leaning against his chest. He didn't try to stop her with empty promises; rather he let her ride out her emotional storm.

The train had pulled away from the Brinsford station by the time John felt Kate relax. It was then that he noticed that she had fallen asleep. He sensitively moved her so that she could sleep while leaning on him.

'It will be all right Kathryn!' He whispered as he brushed a straying hair away from her tear stained face. 'I won't leave you alone. I will make sure that you get safely to your father.' He gently sealed the promise as he placed a kiss on the top of her head. 'I care too much for you to leave you all alone!'

CHAPTER 5

*T*he four hours of train travel, though uneventful, were not without worries. By the time the huge, puffing engine pulled into the platform at the Flinders Street Station, John had allowed a number of concerns to reach levels of anxiety in his mind.

Kate had slept fitfully on his shoulder for the best part of two hours, after they had set out from Brinsford. John had done his best to see that she was comfortable, and not disturbed. That she was still unwell was obvious. If it hadn't have been for all of the worries immediately at hand, John would have been tempted to question the validity of Lady Wallace's code of ethics. But as it was, his mind was too full of what he planned to do once they reached Melbourne.

When Kate finally did wake, John could see that she was mortified to find herself in what could easily have been considered as a position of compromise. She struggled to hold herself upright, stiff and uncomfortable, and he knew that it was only her fierce pride that held her. Several times he was tempted to apologise, but he had no sensible words to use that would ease the situation at all. Anything he could think to say would have only complicated an already awkward and tense scenario.

'Are you feeling any better?' He ventured this question as the train began to pass familiar city landmarks.

For a few moments, Kate grappled for a reasonable answer. In truth she felt every bit as ill as she had done only days before, but to admit that challenged not only her pride, but her sense of moral decency. She recognised only too well how her sickness had thrust her into the position whereby she had become physically reliant on Reverend Laslett – a young man whom she had sought to hate; someone whom she'd wanted to blame for the whole horrible situation. Now to be placed in the position whereby she was totally dependent on him for her every need was almost more than she could cope with. And to add insult to injury, Kate acknowledged with embarrassment her own delirious actions that had caused the Hodges to think the worst of both of them. How was such a simple question, now asked, to be answered?

Because of the difficulty, Kate hesitated, but her concern was clearly etched in her features.

'I think I understand how you must feel,' John ventured, gently, after it was apparent she had no answer.

'How on earth could you possibly understand?' Kate managed to muster just enough indignation to sound convincing. 'You are not the one who has been branded by her father's supposed disgrace. You are not the one who has been left without home or means. You are not the one who now bears marks of her own disgrace.'

'That was all just a misunderstanding. The Hodges have acknowledged that.' John interrupted her tirade.

'I doubt that Lady Wallace will see it that way. Do you know what it was my father did that was enough to have him thrown out so carelessly?'

'I have wondered.' John ventured the answer gingerly.

'Yes! No doubt you have.' Kate was beginning to flag in her account, her emotional energy seeping away, along with her physical strength.

'Let's not discuss it now, Kate. Is it all right for me to call you Kate?'

'What does it matter now?' she murmured. 'The damage has already been done, hasn't it?'

'This is the last we will talk of the issue for now,' John spoke with some authority. 'You are too unwell to be getting yourself so upset. But I will say this, Kate, Lady Wallace will hear the truth, and she will acknowledge it. She must, for if she believes anything else, it implicates the both of us. I know you don't hold me in any great esteem, and I suppose you have good reason, so you will have to accept what you can as consolation. If it is what you will believe, you must know that the least I will do is fight for my own innocence. Do you understand that?'

Kate nodded weakly. Somewhere in the back of her mind, she knew that she must admit some gratitude to the man who was taking such pains to see to her well-being.

As the train pulled into the rail yards, the conductor made his way through the carriage, announcing their impending arrival. John watched as the official performed his duty, and then came to stand adjacent to them.

'Excuse me, sir!' The conductor leaned in their direction. 'I can see that your wife is not at all well. Would you like me to secure a cab for you once we get in to Melbourne?'

As if to silence any objection she may make, John squeezed her hand, before answering the man. 'I would greatly appreciate your service,' he answered.

Kate waited only until the conductor was at the end of the carriage before she made her complaint, lacking in energy, but not in conviction.

'How could you?' she accused. 'You have allowed that man to believe we are man and wife!'

'It would have appeared worse if he believed we were what we are.'

'What do you mean by that?'

'We are unchaperoned for the present. I doubt the kind gentleman would have approved.'

'But you are a minister,' Kate argued.

'That fact didn't alter the Hodges' point of view, did it now?'

Kate paused, considering miserably the predicament that seemed to embroil her. 'You could have told him I was your sister,' she eventually offered.

'Both explanations are a lie, Kate. It is wrong either way. I am sorry, but through the evil of circumstance, you and I have found ourselves in a compromising position. I promise I will take as little time as possible to restore it to rights, but in the meantime, the course of least resistance seems to be the best path to pursue. I'm sure your father will make the allowance this once. If it makes you feel any better, I will correct the conductor's misconception when we see him next.'

Kate wondered briefly if such a confession would be of any benefit, but her condition of fatigue was so overwhelming, that her moment of bad conscience quickly faded away. 'Do whatever you think is right, Reverend,' she whispered.

Getting Kate from the train to the waiting cab proved to be a more difficult exercise than John had at first anticipated. When she had boarded the train, she had, admittedly, leaned heavily on Mr Hodges. But John found that the four hours of travel on top of the emotional trauma had weakened his charge to such an extent that he was obliged to actually carry her. The kind conductor was most gracious in his efforts to make the task easier, inquiring further as to whether he could be of any service. Though thankful for the generous offer, he felt the responsibility in his conscience to be honest.

'Can I send ahead to make arrangements for some-where for you and your wife to stay?'

'You have been most helpful,' John began the hard task of straightening the truth. 'Perhaps you have miscon-strued the situation, sir. The young lady is not my wife, you see. As minister at her parish, she has been left in my charge to be taken to her father. He is here in Melbourne, you understand.'

John watched the man's face for a clue to his reaction, and saw just a tinge of surprise, followed by disappoint-ment.

'I see!' He spoke, perhaps a little less friendly in tone. 'Where shall I tell the cabby her father is?'

'Unfortunately,' John began, his defences rising, 'we have lost track of his whereabouts. The last we heard of him, he had been taken ill, and was housed at St Joseph's Hospice.' John knew that the mere mention of this estab-lishment would make the situation all the more lacking in respectability. Having come from a family considered one of the better class, he was well aware of the reputation St Joseph's bore. Though originally founded and run by the church, St Joseph's was infamous for the manner of soci-ety discards it housed. The gentle, caring monks were not above taking in needy folk from rather dubious back-grounds. They cared for the sick and infirm men and women who had little to their name. Usually the destitute and homeless. John knew this information, and though his mother's analysis echoed briefly in his mind – that they were a worthless bunch of vagrants who deserved every trial that came to them – he held tenaciously to his own private conviction. John admired the workers who gave of themselves till it hurt. He silently applauded those who would give aid of every form, never expecting payment in return. It was a true charity done in Jesus' name.

John was brought back from his reverie just in time to notice the conductor turning to take his leave.

'Thank you, sir, for all your kindness. God bless you, sir.'

Because the man obviously had respect, he turned slightly, and gave an imperceptible nod of his head. It was quite plain to John, though, that he had seen the unsuitableness of their arrangements, and had made his own judgement, just as John had thought he would.

Kate had watched the exchange, and thought she detected the disapproval. She sighed, aware that she, once again, had brought condemnation upon a man who had done nothing but try to help her.

'Reverend Laslett.' She sought to attract his attention once he was seated in the cab.

'Don't try to talk now,' he admonished. 'You've little enough strength as it is.'

'No! I must,' she countered, though feeble in tone. 'You are always apologising for . . . for everything. I know I wanted to blame you for all of our troubles. I wanted to hate you for it.' She paused for breath.

'It's all right.' John patted her hand, as if to reassure.

'It isn't all right. I'm the one who should apologise. I was the one who lied to you in the first place. I invaded your home. I got you into trouble with Lady Wallace. I'm the one who has put you in this place of compromise now. I'm the one who should apologise!' She slumped back in her seat, totally spent.

'I understand, Kate. I appreciate your apology, but I understand why you did it. It wasn't all your fault.'

The pair fell to silence while the sound of horses' hooves clattering on the cobblestones echoed in the air.

John came down the steps of St Joseph's in defeat. The monks remembered Carlton Winston, and had tried to help him to the best of their ability. They had spoken to John of the 'retired' minister's condition, and had indicated that they felt it was not hopeful. When John had asked why he was not with them any more, they revealed news that made the situation even more grim. Because of an epidemic of scarlet fever, St Joseph's had moved all patients out that could possibly be moved. They believed that the Reverend Winston had been removed and settled in the city's poorhouse.

'But can he work for his keep?' John had asked alarmed.

'I seriously doubt it,' the holy brother had answered. 'Perhaps they have accepted him on the basis that he prays and preaches for them. Perhaps he has strength enough to fulfil this duty.'

As John walked back toward the waiting cab, his heart was heavy. Kate needed to be put into the hands of a nurse. She needed to be in bed, and yet the only opportunity that existed was St Joseph's. But the scarlet fever epidemic had used up all available beds. And even if a bed had been available, John was reluctant to leave her in a place where she would easily catch the deadly disease.

'Is he there?' Kate asked the question the moment John climbed back into the cab.

'I'm afraid not.' John answered that much, but was most reluctant to divulge any more. He did not really want Kate to know the depths to which her beloved father had sunk. Kate waited for her companion to say more, but he was too involved with his own thoughts to notice.

There were few choices now available to him. To take Kate to his mother's home was unthinkable, and John quickly cast it from the list of possibilities. His two sisters briefly crossed his mind but the chances of his mother finding out were too great, so they were removed to the last resort list. He thought then of his own church denomination, and the charity services they might provide. But it only took a moment to remember the arrogant Reverend Thatcher, and his manipulative attempts to marry his daughter off to him, to bring John back to reality on that count.

'Where will we find him?' John heard Kate's pathetic plea – the childlike quality of her voice.

'Firstly, I must find a place where you can be nursed back to health.'

Even as he spoke, John hit upon an idea that refused to be pushed out of his mind. He grappled with the dishonesty of it, but argued with himself that he was fast running out of solutions to an urgent problem. As to the rightness of it, he refused to indulge the thought. *No!* He lectured himself. *The first thing is to find a safe place for her to convalesce.*

As the cab pulled up outside the austere building, marked Mercy of Heaven, John pushed aside the last argument in his mind. He knew what this home was built for, and what it represented, but he felt it presented the one and only solution to the immediate problem. He had no doubt that the Sisters would accept Kate Winston into their care. Without answering any of her questions, John lifted Kate from the cab and began to carry her up the steps of the home – the home that was founded and run for unwed mothers.

CHAPTER 6

John had experienced little trouble in installing Kate in the Mercy of Heaven home for unwed mothers. The sister had simply asked him if his charge was in trouble, and he had answered 'yes'. As to the sort of trouble they had meant, he did not bother to elaborate. Kate had been too weak to understand, or to question. She had been taken and put to bed. John saw that the nursing sisters knew what they were about. He heard instructions given and was satisfied that Kate's immediate health needs would be seen to.

As he left the home, his conscience troubled him a little. He knew the implications drawn of even being associated with such a place. He wondered if the sisters had even believed his own story of having the role of concerned clergyman, or if they had assumed more, as seemed to be the common procedure ever since he had come in contact with the girl.

Still, she was safe and well looked after, and John brushed aside the other disquieting thoughts with these congratulations.

By the time John had entered his former home, and had been welcomed by his mother, Kate's concerns held less place in his mind. Of course Mrs Laslett had assumed her son had returned to apologise, and finally come to comply with her original intent. John didn't bother to correct her for the first night. He was not ready to face the barrage of attack he knew would come when he announced his intention to return to Green Valley.

For the next few days that he remained in Melbourne, John did what he could to track down Reverend Winston. As the brothers had prophesied, John found him installed in a poorhouse. He questioned the management as to the reverend's ability to justify his stay. It seemed that they were willing to accept spiritual input, but hoped his family would soon find a way to support him. They spoke strongly to John, imploring him, that if he knew of family, to do everything in his power to restore them. John read the concern behind their plea, and identified an unspoken assumption that the Reverend Winston was dying.

At the end of three days, all John had managed to do was find Kate a place in an establishment of ill repute, and turn up the information that her one and only guardian – her only hope of a secure future – was, in fact, not expected to recover his health. Troubled, John returned to Laslett House. He knew it was a slim chance, but he had to at least try.

'Mother, I wonder if perhaps you might be able to help me with a situation I'm currently dealing with?' He brought the subject up during the breakfast of his fourth day.

'John! I have done my best to influence the bishop in finding you a decent living. I have liaised with Reverend Thatcher to secure a worthy marriage. And what do you do in return?' She paused for effect, her eyes piercing him in a way that spoke of her disapproval. 'What else am I expected to do to help you?'

John was intimidated, and ashamed of himself for being so. He saw the manipulative manner with which his mother sought to get her own way, and he detested his lack of strength in standing up to her. Still he pressed on in his most urgent quest.

'I have a young lady . . .' The words had hardly left his mouth before Mrs Laslett muffled a cry by clapping her hand across her mouth.

'Let me finish, Mother!' John tried to sound stern.

'What about Bernice Thatcher? You've promised her!'

'I promised nothing!' John found himself on the verge of shouting. 'And I'm not talking about marriage. My young lady has nothing to do with me, or marrying me.'

'What then? What else could you possibly be thinking?'

'The young lady is destitute and quite ill. I am responsible for her for the moment.'

'What about her family?' She didn't sound at all sympathetic. 'Surely they are not going to leave her without means.'

'She has only a father, and he, by all accounts, is dying. I daren't even tell the girl. She is not strong enough to take such a shock.'

'Surely her father has made provision for her. There must be servants who will assume the responsibility. Has she no appointed guardian? Whatever are you suggesting, John?'

'I'm not suggesting anything, Mother. All I am asking is if you would be prepared to have her here for a period of time. She needs a place to convalesce, and she has nowhere else to go.'

'Where is she now, then, for heaven's sake?'

John pulled up short in the discussion, unwilling to reveal Kate's current whereabouts. The mere suggestion would send his mother into a fit of hysterics, of that he was certain.

'Well, John. I must know. Where is this young woman, of whom you speak?'

'I've had to place her in a charity hospice!'

'A hospice! John! You know what I think about those sorts of places. If people are sick, let them be looked after in their own homes, by their own people.'

'She has no people! She has no home!'

'And why not? What sort of woman is this? What are you proposing?'

'Perhaps this is not a situation you will be able to help me with after all.'

'I can't leave it at that, young man! I *will* know what sort of people you are mixed up with. This is the Laslett name we are talking about. Whatever do you mean by associating with the sorts of people who use charity homes? Reverend Thatcher would not be seen anywhere near such an establishment!'

'No! I daresay he wouldn't.' John sounded defea-   ted.

'I don't want you going anywhere near one of them again. What say someone might recognise you? Goodness me, John. Can you imagine the uproar I would have, trying to explain it away?'

John made the best excuse he could in the face of such a tirade. He could just imagine the storm he'd have faced if he'd mentioned just which charity home Kate was in. He didn't think he had the emotional energy to fight that sort of battle. As he went to bed that night, he decided there was nothing left that he could do in Melbourne. Hating his own inadequacies, and the feelings of failure that he felt, John decided that he would return to Green Valley and try to forget that he'd even tried to help those less fortunate than himself.

'I tried, Lord!' He struggled to excuse himself in prayer as his sense of right and wrong plagued his dreams. 'What else can I do?'

By the second day at Mercy of Heaven, Kate had regained a certain amount of strength, enough at least to conduct intelligent conversation. She wondered, at first, why the Sisters of Mercy were so dour-faced and exuding disapproval in whatever they did. It didn't take her long to realise what it was that the sisters were trying to do.

They are making it clear to me that they condemn my actions, Kate thought. *That would be all perfectly justifiable if I was really in the condition they assumed.* Once Kate had seen the other young women housed at the hospice, she saw where it was that Reverend Laslett had left her. At first she was shocked to the core. She wanted to argue and defend herself, but her first such effort was met with stone cold hardness.

'Accept your punishment as it comes to you, young lady,' the sister lectured. 'It won't do you any good denying the truth.'

Kate saw then and there that only time would vindicate her. She watched the sadness and resignation in the eyes of the young, defenceless women, all of them hopeless in their state. It didn't take her long to regain the old bitterness toward John.

How could he have left me here, of all places? she asked herself over and over at night-time. All of these thoughts drew their own conclusions. John had lied to her and had left her in the worst position of compromise of all. Kate's anger burned against him.

As the weeks passed, and her health gradually returned, any chance that John might have had to redeem himself vanished. He did not return. She heard nothing from the outside. The routine in the home was established for those well enough to work. Chores were assigned and it was expected that the lot would be borne without complaint. Kate helped in every area of the home; in the kitchen; in the

laundry; but it was in the nursery that she was most affected. She helped tend to the tiny, unwanted infants. The
mothers were not allowed to see their children once they
had given birth. Their job was to recover and then to re-
emerge into the world as if nothing had ever happened. It
was left to people like Kate to look after the babies. The
whole process was heart breaking. Sometimes, she caught
one of the sisters showing an amount of compassion on the
children, but she was aware that it was generally frowned
upon. These were bastard children; the fruit of sin. It
seemed that the unspoken law was that they must know it
from the very beginning. Kate learned only too soon not to
become emotionally attached to the little ones. The first
time she had shown some affection, she was to be grieved
when the child was adopted out within a week.

Kate conversed little with anyone in the home. She
quickly learned to keep any thoughts or feelings to herself.
This was a place of disgrace and punishment, and those
who were unfortunate enough to find themselves here
needed to acknowledge the grimness of that fact. Often
Kate felt indignant, not just on her own innocent behalf,
but also on behalf of the young girls who were in a condition brought about by two people. It had to be acknowledged, she felt, that there were a whole lot of immoral men
living life as normal, who had put these women in this
plight. Still Kate knew that she was not in any position to
be crusading. She bided her time and waited for enough
months to go by before she could prove to the stern matron
in charge that it was as she had maintained all along.

'Why on earth would Reverend Laslett tell me you
were with child, if you were not?' the matron asked, not
amused by the discovery.

'He told you that?' Kate was incredulous.

'Well he certainly led me to believe that was the case.

Perhaps it is that you have just lost the baby.'

'There was never any baby!' Kate cried, frustrated. 'I have never been married.'

'Neither have most of the young women here.'

'Please,' Kate continued. 'I came to Melbourne in search of my father. I was very ill. Reverend Laslett promised he would help me, and he left me here. I don't know why, but I can't stay here.'

'On that point we agree,' the older woman barked. 'Have you no other place to go?'

'Nowhere. My father is my last hope.'

'I will write to Reverend Laslett and ask him what he intends to do about the situation. Until we have a reply, I trust you will continue to help us. I must admit you have worked hard and efficiently. Perhaps you have found a calling.'

Kate heard the analysis, and cringed. She knew she could never stay in this place in any capacity. She could not bear the grief and hopelessness of the young women as they were processed. She could not bear the mark of illegitimacy that each infant had stamped eternally on their tiny character. She did not make her thoughts known to the sister in charge, but agreed to wait for a reply from Green Valley. She hoped that John had a good reason for what he did – but then, she also hoped that he didn't. It would make it so much easier for her to go on resenting him.

The moment the letter arrived, John knew that he could no longer ignore all those inner voices of moral sense that had desperately tried to regain his focus. Once again he was brought face to face with his own inadequacy – his inability to bring a suitable solution to a difficult situation.

The imagined ghosts of the manse had been nothing compared with his sense of shame that would keep him tossing half the night. He was not proud of having left Kate under false pretences, and having failed to keep his promise to her. He was ashamed – thoroughly ashamed, and yet, even as he stared at the letter, he continued in hopelessness. With the many questions and doubts still raging for attention in his mind, John set out in quest of counsel.

'You're askin' us, laddie?' Mr Hodges sounded astonished as he heard the young minister's tale. 'You're the spiritual leader here. You're the one who is supposed to be able to guide and direct the rest of us!'

'I know!' John sounded desperate. 'It's the truth, but I am at a loss. There is nothing in any of my seminary notes that covers this sort of situation.'

'What about your superiors in the church? What have they to say on the issue?' The older gentleman seemed willing to at least prod for answers.

'I haven't the courage to admit to them that I am even in such a predicament.' John's tone was forlorn. 'I sought help from my mother before I left Melbourne, and she made it quite clear what was accepted as decent.' He sighed in memory of the defeat. 'It would seem that the best policy for such a situation is "out of sight, out of mind."'

'But that's preposterous!' Mrs Hodges threw in her opinion, having listened in silence thus far.

'Is it, Mrs Hodges?' John suddenly felt a fire of conviction. 'Don't tell me you have not practised this policy yourselves at times. What about your desperate hurry to send Kate away from Green Valley? She could hardly stand on her feet, yet you insisted she must be got away. Why?'

'You know why!' Mrs Hodges defended. 'I'm not fool enough to imagine Lady Wallace will suddenly develop a merciful nature. She has her standards, and we comply, or . . .'

'Exactly!' John sounded satisfied. 'The attitude of those above us seems to be quite congruent with Lady Wallace herself. There is decency; there are standards; our job is to aid those who stay within those guidelines. But the rest . . .' John left the thought hanging.

'You did promise the lass.' Hodges eventually broke the thoughtful silence.

'*We* promised her,' John carefully reminded him. 'Remember? All three of us had a hand in reassuring her that we would see her safe to her father.'

'Yes, yes! You're quite right. We all promised.'

'So, what is it that we can do now? We simply cannot leave her where she is.'

'I should say not!' Mrs Hodges sounded indignant.

'Would you be prepared to have both the reverend and his daughter come back here, to Green Valley?' John introduced the only idea he'd been able to formulate.

'Where do you suppose they'd be able to stay?' Mrs Hodges didn't seem overly warm to the idea.

'Hasn't Reverend Winston any friends left here?'

'Oh, aye! He has friends aplenty.' Hodges sounded certain. 'But as his daughter already found out, none of them'd be able to afford to feed one more mouth, let alone two.'

'But surely, among the better established families . . .'

'No, sir!' Hodges seemed adamant. 'Those that have enough, or are set up well like, have Lady Wallace's favour. I doubt you'd find one who'd risk goin' against her – and that's what it'd be if you brought the reverend back to the Valley. She got rid o' him from his position, and made it nigh impossible for his daughter to stay. I take it ye are aware of that fact.'

'But couldn't she be wrong?' John's tone was full of frustration.

'Is that something you want to bring up with her?' Hodges sounded as if the question should end the argument, and John had to silently admit to himself that he was not willing to take the matter that far.

'Would you be prepared to have them stay here with you?' John turned his last hopeful request toward the hostess.

'Here?' Mrs Hodges sounded incredulous. 'Haven't you been listenin' to a thing my man's been a tellin' ya?'

John's shoulders slumped as he realised there was little to be gained by discussing the issue further with these folks.

'What'll you be doin' about the lass, then?' Hodges asked as he escorted his visitor to the door.

'I don't know, Hodges. I simply don't know if there's anything I can do. Perhaps it would be better to just put her out of my mind.'

'I don't know if that'd be the right thing to do.' Mrs Hodges made the comment as she watched him depart.

'No! Probably not the right thing,' John agreed, 'but it would certainly be easier and cause less conflict.'

As John mounted his horse and made ready to ride away from the gatekeeper's lodge, he wondered if he'd gained any wisdom at all by his visit.

'Don't forget who it is you work for, son,' Hodges offered quietly, once he was away from the house.

'I know!' He nodded. 'Lady Wallace has her standards.'

'No, boy! You're a minister, are ye not? 'Tis the Almighty I'm referrin' to. He must have a solution. Surely. 'Tis his heart to help the poor, ain't it?'

John rode away with this piece of advice ringing in his ears. *You must have an answer,* he prayed, *for if you don't, pity help Kate and her father.*

CHAPTER 7

John could not believe he had just done what he had done. He stood staring stupidly at the frail gentleman seated before him and waited for an answer. When time seemed to drag on painfully, John decided to retract his request

'I'm sorry, sir. I should never have presumed upon you. This must all be a horrible problem for you to face.'

'Wait just a moment!' Carlton Winston issued his direction with a struggle for breath. 'Let me just understand a few things.'

John waited for his condemnation to come from the older gentleman. He noticed his own heart hammering wildly, and his palms become sweaty.

'I can't say I'm happy, on the one hand, to hear about the present condition of my daughter's reputation,' he began, with great effort. 'But I suppose, on the other, I've only myself to blame for it, haven't I?'

'Circumstance seems to have sided against you, sir.' John tried to ease the sick man's self-recriminations.

'Circumstance and Lady Wallace, I should say. Not that she hadn't a perfect right,' he hurried on.

'I don't quite understand, sir.' John allowed his puzzlement to show on his face.

'Well, my boy, I suppose, if you are to be my son-in-law, you had better know the whole truth.'

'Do you mean to say, you agree with my proposal?' John didn't know if he should be thankful or horrified.

'Do you love my daughter?' Carlton asked the question, unashamedly.

'Truthfully?'

'Is there any other answer?'

John took a deep breath to fortify his courage. 'I don't really know, sir.'

'Then why ask for her hand in marriage?'

'I cannot think of another way to prevent her from falling further into ruin, or another way to help you.'

'Why should it be any of your concern in the first place?' The senior reverend seemed ruthless in his interrogation.

'Isn't it the concern of any servant of God to see to the welfare of the sick and orphaned?'

'A good theological answer, young man, but not necessarily a good basis for marriage.'

'I'm sorry.' John seemed genuinely repentant. 'It is all I can think of for the moment. If it does not meet with your approval, I shall leave you both alone.'

'You have no concern for where Katie is currently situated?'

'Of course I am concerned. I was the one who put her there. Look! I am sorry for a lot of things, Reverend Winston, not the least of which is having turned the pair of you out of your home.'

'You cannot wear the responsibility for that unfortunate affair.'

'Yes and no! It was not my decision, but nevertheless, I am the one who has been landed with the responsibility for your daughter, rightly or wrongly.'

'And so you want to marry her?'

'As I said before, I do not know. I don't even know if desire has anything to do with it in the first place. My mother certainly believes that the only necessary requirement for marriage is if she approves.' John's tone had risen with his frustration to such a point that a staff member had come across cautioning him not to excite the patient.

'Now, now!' Carlton muttered. 'There's no need for us to be getting all agitated. You've been good enough to see to her welfare so far. I'm prepared to give you further leave where she is concerned. For all her faults, Lady Wallace is a good judge of character when it comes to choosing her clergy.'

'So, where do we go from here?' John asked the question, not at all sure whether he should be relieved or worried.

'First of all, allow me to relay to you my sordid history, and then give you the chance to decide whether you still want to be associated with us as a family.'

John nodded his acquiescence, and took a seat right opposite the reverend.

'I was about your age when I was first invited to serve at the Green Valley Parish. I had not been long married, and was totally unaware that my new bride was un-happy – no! Unhappy doesn't really describe the way she felt. Appalled would be a better word. She was from a well-to-do family here in Melbourne. Ah! My poor Lizzie.' Carlton sighed at the memory. 'I'm afraid she pleased herself more than her parents when it came to choosing a poor clergyman for a husband. Her father was not the most understanding sort, and more or less cursed her to her fate. That was me – her fate. When we arrived in Green Valley, Lizzie was already with child. At first she did just what any man would expect of a wife. She could not be faulted. But then, after Katie was born, she began to complain. I listened with all the compassion I would have wanted others to listen to me. I heard her pain and misery at being separated from all she knew and loved.

I listened with sympathy, but there was little I could do.

'Eventually, a letter arrived from her mother. Mrs Oliver pleaded with me to send their little girl home for a visit. It appeared that her father had taken ill, and he desired reconciliation for obvious reasons. Of course, I was not going to deny her that much, and so I borrowed money from Lady Wallace herself to help me send Lizzie home to her parents. My own dear mother had been with us ever since Lizzie's confinement, and so she agreed to stay on to look after Katie. I missed my wife from the moment she left, but I was not about to prevent her from taking this precious opportunity.

'I waited and waited for word to come back. But Lizzie never wrote. She did not let me know that she had arrived. She did not send word to indicate when she would return. Katie was only a few months old at the time, so I was seriously worried. I felt sure that something disastrous must have occurred to have prevented a young mother from inquiring after her baby. Of course I sent several letters. When none of them were answered, I became frantic with worry. Everyone knew how distraught I was.

'It was Hodges and his wife who suggested I go to Melbourne to see for myself that everything was all right. Once again, I had to borrow the money to make the trip.' The ageing father paused at this point, as if the sorrow of his discovery was too much for him.

'Was your wife ill, sir?' John found he could not bear the suspense any longer.

'If only it had been that simple,' Carlton whispered, regret clearly evident in his tone. 'No, son! It was far worse. I was not in Melbourne one day before I discovered what had really happened. She was not to be found with her parents as I'd thought. They were in reasonable health, but not at all happy to see me. They blamed me right from the outset. They said it was my fault that it had all happened. If only I had left her where she belonged, none of this would have ever happened, they said.'

'What? What happened?' John was intrigued.

'Lizzie had been to visit her parents, and had come in contact with an old family acquaintance. It was another young man of some disreputable character, who had sought her hand some months before I had happened into her life. Of course, her parents had denied consent then, and her sudden wild intention to marry a poor clergyman had seemed a far lesser evil to them, when I did happen along. But when she returned to Melbourne, the young scoundrel had introduced himself back into her society again. Apparently, she was hell bent on seeing him, despite her father's warnings. I could not have been more shocked when I found out, but more so when I discovered that the wife I adored had run away with a former lover. What was I to do? Nobody knew where they had gone. No one seemed willing to discuss it openly. It almost seemed as if they would have preferred I didn't remind them of the disgrace she had brought on their family.'

'And so, what did you do?' John felt the pain of the storyteller.

'Much the same as I'm doing now, son. I was hopeless and lost and hardly had the courage to go on, yet somehow, I wandered back to Green Valley. There was Katie to consider, after all. I left some sketchy instructions with the Olivers to let me know if any information came to light as to Lizzie's whereabouts.'

'What has this to do with your recent eviction? Surely Lady Wallace could not have held a grudge all those years.'

'No one in the Valley knew the truth, son. When I drifted home, I was like a grieving man. I was a grieving man, but the folk who greeted me assumed for the wrong reason. It was Hodges who asked me first. All I could tell him was that she was gone. He obviously misunderstood, and deduced that Lizzie had died. I went into seclusion, and it was almost a week before I realised that my parishioners had gone into mourning with me, for the death of my wife. When I comprehended what was happening, I didn't have the heart to tell them the truth. They all believed that my wife had died, and that I was left with a small child to raise. My mother didn't ask; the Hodges didn't pry; Lady Wallace offered her sincere condolences, and hopes that I would soon recover my spirits. In the light of what the alternative would have been, had they known the truth, I decided to let the falsehood continue. For the last nineteen years, the people of Green Valley have lived under the impression that I was a widower.'

'And this last year?' John had to know the full story.

'I was sent word that Lizzie was dead. It was too late to call back the lie then. I could have continued to cover the story up, but my dull conscience got the better of me. I confessed the truth to the church board, which of course included Lady Wallace. She was incensed that I could have lived such a lie for so long. When I left the Valley to go to the funeral, I did not know what she would do when I returned. But as it was, I never returned. I was taken ill here, in Melbourne. Lizzie's family might have helped me, but they chose to disassociate themselves from their daughter's funeral, and from me. I sent word to Hodges, but never received a reply. I think perhaps you know the rest of the story from there.'

'I think perhaps I do.' John sounded sorrowful, and looked thoughtfully out of the window. The pair waited in silence for some moments before Carlton began to speak again.

'And so, young man. Having heard the full account of my sin, are you still willing to marry into my fam-ily?'

'It was wrong to deceive all those people for all those years.'

'You don't have to tell me, my boy. I'm well aware that what I did was wrong. I sometimes wonder if this current illness might not be God's way of paying me back.'

'Do you really think that God would inflict us with such suffering?'

'Sometimes I have been tempted to question him, yes! But no! In my heart I know the truth. I have sinned, yes. But my current sickness is nothing more than a fact of life. If anything, God has answered my prayers.'

'Answered your prayers! How?' John asked.

'He has sent you, hasn't he? An honest, upstanding young man who is willing to marry my poor Katie, and who is willing to take care of her for the rest of her life. Is that not so?'

John paused in thought for just a moment. 'Yes! That is so, reverend. All that remains is to convince your Katie that I mean no harm to her. That I sincerely want the best for her well-being!'

'If anything, John Laslett, you have my wholehearted support. I will pray for your success.'

'You don't sound confident.' John made the observation.

'Confident!' Carlton chuckled. 'I know my own daughter, man. She has a stubborn streak in her that would defy the best of them. If you can overcome that, then I will be sure you are the man for the job!'

John came away from the poorhouse not too certain. He still wondered what on earth had possessed him to ask Kate's father for her hand in marriage. Of course he acknowledged that it was the only reasonable solution to their dilemma, but on reflection, it did seem like a rather complicated and permanent commitment for himself. He knew that it was not just his sense of goodwill that had prompted him. He had to admit that his care and concern for Kate was beyond what he would normally feel for a parishioner. But as to whether it constituted love or not, was an issue that remained to be tested.

And tested it would be – very soon. John looked up from the cab window to see the austere and imposing façade of the Mercy of Heaven home.

How could I have left her here? John berated himself for the umpteenth time. *And now what am I supposed to say to the good sisters who run the home*?

But John was not to be turned away from his moral duty. He had suffered too many sleepless nights to turn back now.

'I do apologise for my having allowed you to believe the worst.' John was thoroughly intimidated by the matron's iron glare. 'I was in a desperate situation, you see. Miss Winston was so ill, and I had nowhere else I could leave her.'

'Perhaps if you had told us the truth from the start, we may have made temporary arrangements for her.'

'Would you have done that, honestly?' John somehow doubted the claim.

At the forwardness of his question, especially from his position of guilt, John thought he would receive further censure. But after a strained moment of silence, the matron replied. 'No! I suppose we would have put you off as well. It is an unfortunate thing, Reverend. There always seems to be more need for charity help than there is help available.'

'I have discovered this fact,' John answered without malice. 'Nonetheless, I acknowledge my fault in having misled you.'

'Miss Winston has suffered a great indignity, sir,' the officious Sister went on. 'I hope you realise that. She is well within her rights to be very angry with you. This is not the sort of place that one is even proud to work in. It is a home marked with contempt in every aspect. I do hope that you will convey her straight to her father, and not trouble her with your own presence for too long.'

John wanted to give her that assurance, just to get the transaction completed quickly, but his newly formed pledge of honesty prevented him. 'I understand what you have just told me, madam,' he began.

'But?' She interrupted him with plain suspicion.

'I have just spoken with her father, and gained his permission to ask for her hand in marriage.'

'And you think she will accept?' The Sister seemed ready to burst with sarcastic mirth.

'I think she will be outraged, offended and ready to order me from her sight. Unfortunately, there are few alternatives open at present.'

'You are going to great lengths to appease your guilty conscience, sir,' the woman seemed intent on speaking her mind, 'or is it that you really love the girl?'

Here was the question again, and for the second time, John did not really know if he knew the answer. Was he just trying to appease his guilty conscience? And if so, weren't there better ways for him to do it without him being so lastingly obligated?

'Well?' The sister waited with obvious delight at his discomfiture.

'This is the path I wish to pursue,' John finally answered with a reasonable amount of conviction. 'The final decision lies with Miss Winston. If she refuses my proposal, then I can do nothing more for her, or for her father. I guess it is that simple.'

But when Kate was eventually brought to him, John's courage failed miserably. He saw instantly the resentment that burned in her eyes. He saw the hardness in her face – a hardness born of sorrow and regret.

'Well, Reverend, are you going to tell her, or shall I?' The sister's tone revealed her contempt.

'May I have a few moments alone with Miss Winston?' John fought to maintain composure.

'Very well!'

Kate hardly flinched as the head of the home flounced out of the office. She continued to stare straight ahead, as if she had already made up her mind that she would not look at her so-called 'rescuer'.

'Kate . . .'

'Miss Winston, to you!' Kate was ruthless in her tone.

'Miss Winston, it is then.' John bowed in apology. 'There are no words that can possibly make up for the wrong that has been done to you.'

'The wrong that you have done to me!' Kate accused. 'You lied to me, and then you left me here!' She spat the last word out with disdain.

'I was wrong.' John didn't try to justify himself. 'I can't do anything but beg your forgiveness.'

'Forgiveness?' Kate tried to sound unbelieving. 'Do you know what several months in a place like this teaches you? There is no such thing as forgiveness. Not once you've passed that doorstep. You are branded, innocent or not!'

'Kate, don't! It can't be too late!'

'Too late for what, may I ask?'

'I have done you wrong, yes! Others have done you wrong also, but never let bitterness breed so carelessly in your heart. It doesn't just hurt me, though I know that's what you want. Listen to me! It will kill you. It will poison your very soul until there is nothing lovely left.'

'So what is it you think I should do? Do you think I should just pretend the last few months have not happened? And then what? I'll just walk out those front doors and go where? Where will I go? Is there any other place in the world for me? I don't think so, is there, Reverend Laslett?'

John had almost accepted defeat when the sister walked back into the room.

'Well? What is her answer, Reverend?' she asked, coldly.

'Answer to what?' Kate flung her question toward him. 'What do you think I can give you now?'

'Hasn't he told you?' The sister seemed smug. 'The reverend wants to marry you!'

CHAPTER 8

⚜

John rode next to Kate in the cab, a stony silence thick around them. He struggled with his own thoughts in a furious battle. One part of him wanted to leave the situation and run back to the relative peace of Green Valley. It was this part that flinched in the face of visible resentment. But the other part of him, the part he wanted to grow, held him to his set course. It was this element in him that argued for more. It seemed to lecture him on the evils of being double minded; it demanded of him more when it came to standing up for what he believed to be right.

John recognised his past weakness. It was the same frailty of character that had allowed his mother to manipulate him for so many years, and more recently had allowed Lady Vera Wallace to dictate terms, regardless of his own convictions. John saw it and despised it. In his own mind, he felt it was time for him to hold firm to what was right, and to stand against the many emotional barbs that were thrown his way. And in the present instance, he knew that it was right to at least bring Kate to a conference with her father. As to more, it was for her to decide.

Without a word being spoken between them, John assisted his charge from the cab. He noticed, with sorrow, that she quickly and sharply withdrew her hand from his, the moment her foot held the pavement. *I will stand firm*, John quietly encouraged himself as he turned to pay the cabby.

'You have not seen your father for some time,' John broke the atmosphere, just before they entered the building. 'I'm afraid you will be shocked when you see just how much he has deteriorated.'

Kate heard the words, but chose, in her fury, not to respond. She heeded John's warning, but was determined not to give him the satisfaction of knowing that she had received anything from him. She had decided to do everything in her power to make him feel the anguish she had suffered the past few months.

But Kate's angry façade quickly faded when she saw her father. Regardless of John's warning, Kate was shocked. When she had last seen her father, he had been healthy and active, but now he was reduced to a shell of the man he once was.

'Papa!' She gave a small cry, and knelt immediately at his side. 'Oh, Papa!'

Carlton reached out his feeble hand to touch his daughter's cheek. 'What's all this fuss, Katie?' he asked with feeling.

'Look at you, Papa. I must get you out of this place, and home where you belong.'

'So you've accepted John, I take it.' Carlton sounded pleased.

But at his words, Kate was brought up short. She had not expected that her father would actually want to go along with Reverend Laslett's absurd proposal. She felt sure that once they had reunited, her father would find another way to take care of their problem.

'No! I have not accepted him. Neither will I ever. Don't you know what he has done to me?' Anger burned in Kate's breast, immediately assuming that John had lied to her father.

'What has happened has not been John's fault, child.' Carlton sounded firm. 'He did what he could to see to your well-being.'

'You call placing me in a home for unwed mothers, seeing to my well-being.' Her tone was full of venom, and she didn't care that John stood behind them, capable of hearing her every word.

'If you refuse to see reason, Katie, there is little hope for either of us. You must understand that.'

'There must be another way,' Kate argued. 'If I wanted to marry, that man would be the last person I would consider.'

John could not pretend her words did not hurt him, though he tended to blame himself more than her. 'Reverend Winston?' He stepped forward to interrupt their argument. 'If it will help the situation any, we can make it a temporary arrangement.'

'What do you have in mind, John?' Carlton was open and willing to consider anything at this point.

'As you will be coming with us, you may act as a witness. The marriage will last only until you have found a more suitable arrangement.'

'Are you suggesting that it be a marriage of convenience?' Carlton sounded unsure.

'I have seen it happen before. Sometimes they last, but I've known of cases where the marriage has been annulled. We will never be alone. You may be certain that everything is above board.'

'You can't be serious!' Kate broke loose of her mental stupor. 'How many suitors do you think will come courting a "married woman"? How can I ever improve my situation when I'm legally obligated to you?'

'Katie!' Carlton's voice rose to its full height, considering his fragile condition. 'I won't have you insulting this good man. You cannot throw his honest attempts to help us back in his face.'

'But marriage, Papa . . .' Kate relented only slightly. 'Haven't I heard enough of your wedding services to know what marriage means?'

'I hope so.' He answered his daughter with authority.

'Out of your own mouth, Papa, you've maintained over and over that a wife must love, honour and respect her husband.'

Carlton nodded his agreement.

'Then I cannot marry this man under any circumstances. I have no respect for him whatsoever. Without respect, how can there be honour? He is a weak willed man who thinks first of himself.'

'Katie! That is enough. You have no right to that opinion. It simply isn't true. You are bringing me to the point where I feel I must insist on this alliance. John has offered you a marriage of convenience, and I have decided we will accept. Do you understand me?'

Kate was angry and hurt. A rebellion bubbled up in her, but she knew enough to know she could not defy her father. The worst she could do was storm out of the room, leaving the two men to regret the whole incident.

'Are we doing the right thing, sir?' John's tone was heavy with doubt. 'I want to be able to help you both. If only there was another way.'

'This will be a suitable arrangement, John.' Carlton sounded certain.

'But she hates me!'

'John, my boy. Perhaps she thinks she hates you. At the moment, you are a safe target for all of her hurt and bitterness. As her minister, and more importantly as her husband, you will teach her how to deal with that hurt, and how to let go of that bitterness.'

'You sound so confident,' John sighed. 'At the moment I feel hurt myself. How can I teach her anything when she won't even so much as look at me?'

'Time, John. Time will yield a lot of things.'

'If there is time.' Doubt was still plain in his tone.

'There will be time. There are no opportunities for her outside this marriage. None whatsoever.'

'I regret that we will have a loveless marriage. She deserves more.'

'Loveless?' Carlton caught John's gaze. 'This marriage won't be loveless. You have already proven your love for her over and over. Haven't you seen that? You do love her, don't you, son?'

John had no words with which to deny the charge. If love was the crime, then let him be guilty. 'Yes! I love her,' he quietly admitted.

<hr>

For two ministers to be standing in a registry office for a wedding, something must have been amiss. But John had insisted that the wedding could not be performed in a church. He did not want to make any vows before God that he could not keep. As it was, he found it difficult to repeat vows before a justice of the peace. He wanted to mean every word, but was reluctant, especially when it came to the 'until death do us part' clause. He wondered just how long it would take for Kate to find a more suitable location. Having admitted his love for her made it all the more difficult. Kate mumbled the words expected of her. It was apparent that she was fulfilling an obligation to her father, and that she had no sincerity in her vows.

'You may kiss your bride.' The celebrant mindlessly uttered the order. John looked first to his new father-in-law, and saw him nod, as if to encourage him to follow the usual procedure. Leaning reluctantly towards Kate, he was surprised when she brought her head close to his. She allowed him to kiss her lightly on the cheek, and then took advantage of the closeness of his ear. 'I know just what your worthless promises mean!' She hissed the words for him alone to hear.

John reeled with the pain of what she meant. *Have I made a huge mistake*? He asked himself. *How long can I endure the pain of knowing she despises me so much*?

John didn't know what the justice must have thought as they left his chambers. Kate supported her father on one side, as they left, and John took his other arm. Carlton was very weak, and the exertion of having travelled to the wedding ceremony, and now to be settled somewhere else, was certainly taking its toll.

'I have made arrangements for us to stay with my sister for the time being.'

John felt obliged to inform his new family.

'Did we have to get married for that?' Kate was allowing her resentment full reign, as evidenced by her malicious tone.

'Katie!' Carlton's rebuke was lacking in strength, and Kate regretted having upset him.

'I don't expect you will understand it all,' John began to explain, patiently. 'When I asked my mother to help you those months ago, she made it quite clear to me that she would have nothing to do with beggars. She has a reputation, and she will fight tooth and nail to preserve it. To have placed you with Sandra, back then, would have been to flaunt her wishes. I could not go against her demands.'

'No! You wouldn't!'

'Katie! Will you not be reasonable!'

'I'm sorry, Papa.' There was repentance in her tone, but John knew that it didn't extend as far as to him.

'You may not think it much, Kate,' John continued, 'but I have already defied my mother by marrying you.'

'So, why couldn't you have defied her before?' Kate could not contain her poisonous tongue.

'To ask Sandra to take in an unrelated beggar would have been unthinkable. To ask her to take in my wife and father-in-law will cause a family uproar, but they will not refuse.'

'So your sister is like your mother, then?' Kate continued cruelly.

'Sandra is as different from her as night is from day. Sandra would have wanted to take you in in the first place, but her husband would not have allowed it. He is a good man, but he is a snob. That is one of the few points where he and my mother see eye to eye.'

'Katie, you must stop now.' Carlton spoke quietly, but with authority. 'I cannot bear any more argument. Let us just be thankful that we have a place to go.'

CHAPTER 9

Traces of shame crept over Kate as she was lovingly greeted by her new sister-in-law. Sandra Allenby expressed her delight openly, and hugged Kate with genuine affection.

'John,' Sandra scolded. 'Why wasn't I invited to the wedding?'

Kate waited in fear for John to spill out the whole horrible story, and was amazed when he finally did answer. 'I'm sorry, dear,' he answered, again, genuine affection apparent. 'I would have loved to have had you stand with us, but knowing Mother's reaction, it would have made a miserable day of it for my wife.'

'We need not have told her.' Sandra's tone became conspiratorial. 'Never mind!' She threw off the melancholy tone. 'You have brought her straight to me, and that is all that matters now. Oh, Kate! You are so beautiful.' Sandra gave the compliment with ease. 'Phooey on Mother and her arrangements. I love you already.'

Kate sensed, rather than saw, her father's undeniable pleasure. Acknowledging that only added to her sense of remorse.

'Pardon my cutting your celebration short, Sandra,' John interrupted her, 'but Reverend Winston is quite done in! Could you show us his room so that he can rest?'

Without further delay, Sandra had a servant carry their few belongings up the grand staircase. John assisted another manservant in helping his father-in-law up to his room. Kate followed quietly along behind. She had said so many nasty things about John and his sister that she felt ready to melt with embarrassment.

'When will you introduce your lovely Kate to Mother?' Sandra asked the question later, as they drank tea together.

'I'm not so certain that Mother will want to meet her, once she learns that I have jilted Bernice.'

'Never mind Bernice. I doubt her father would have allowed the two of you to marry anyway, despite all of Mother's intentions. You must take Kate across town to meet Mother tomorrow.'

Kate swallowed nervously. She was already quite intimidated by the grandeur of Sandra's home, let alone coming to Laslett House to be introduced as Mrs Laslett, no less.

But she need not have feared, as John stated his intentions clearly. 'I'm afraid that introduction will have to wait for another time. I will be leaving for Green Valley tomorrow.'

'What are you thinking, John?' Sandra sounded amazed. 'You cannot mean to take Reverend Winston on such a trip so soon. He is too ill.'

'I'm sorry. I have not made myself clear. I'm hoping it will be all right for Kate and her father to stay with you here, while I go and make preparations at the manse for our return.'

'Of course it will be all right, but how can you leave your wife so soon?' Sandra sounded confused. If she had chanced a glance across to the new wife, she would have seen the different shades of emotion that crossed her face, as each piece of information was revealed. If Kate had been honest with herself, she would have seen the opportunity that John was presenting to her – a chance to spend time alone with her father; a chance for him to gain strength. But as it was, she allowed bitter thoughts of desertion to colour her judgement.

By the time dinner was over, and Kate had been introduced to Sandra's husband, Leonard, she was ready to escape from the confinement of having to be polite. All she wanted to do was to get away from John and his family. It was not easy holding her grudge when all they could do was offer her kindness and hospitality.

'Have you enough energy to listen to some music, Kate?' Sandra asked the question. 'My husband and I quite enjoy singing together of an evening.'

'Perhaps Kate would prefer to get an early night.' John cut across his sister's suggestion with his own.

'Of course! How thoughtless of me. By all means, Kate.'

Kate was dismayed when she understood what they were all thinking. This, after all, was her wedding day. She did not, however, make any stinging remarks in their presence. She had already decided to withhold them until she could express herself fully.

John excused them politely, and offered Kate his arm as they left the drawing room. It took all of Kate's will power to accept this physical contact, as every thing in her rebelled. But she resolved to play the game John had made up for them.

'So! What of your promise now?' Kate flung the question at him the instant the bedroom door was closed.

'Which promise are you referring to now?' John asked, tired patience straining his speech.

'You told my father this would be a temporary arrangement. You can't think that he will let you sleep here with me.'

'I don't intend to, Kate. If you want, I will tell my sister the truth about us, and we can take it from there, however . . .' He left the sentence hanging. He was worn out having to face her continual barrage of opposition and abuse. In truth, he couldn't wait to leave in the morning. For a moment, he wondered just how long he dare leave the pair with his sister. He calculated in his mind the longest period he felt would be seen as reasonable, and began to look forward to that length of time in peace.

'Do you intend to leave us here indefinitely? What is it now? Out of sight, out of mind?'

John cringed when he heard the very principle he'd recited used as a summary of his intentions. It was as if this antagonistic woman had read his mind.

'You will believe whatever you want to believe, won't you, Kate? It doesn't matter what I say on any issue, you are determined to twist it until I am the villain. At the moment I am too tired to even bother trying to make you understand.' With that said John picked up his own valise and left the room.

Kate stared, dumbfounded, as the door closed after him. It took her a long moment of thought to comprehend what John had actually done. He had shown her, in dramatic effect, that he would not take any more of her verbal abuse. Once again, shame flooded in to rebuke her. She knew that she was behaving like a spoiled child, and yet the bitterness had taken such root, and when fuelled by her foolish pride, it seemed impossible to behave any other way.

Turning slowly around, Kate saw the room Sandra had made up for them. It was obviously set up to be a bridal suite – the bed was carefully made up and decorated with a bunch of roses. Next to the bed, on a small table, she had set a bottle of champagne and glasses, and a small card wishing them both all happiness in the future.

'Happiness!' Kate recited sadly. 'What hope is there for happiness now?'

John spent an uncomfortable and restless night on the floor in Carlton's room. He hadn't bothered to wake the older man when he'd crept in the night before, and he didn't bother waking him now, as he prepared to leave. He knew that his father-in-law, at least, would understand his sneaking away before dawn.

'Don't take it too hard, son.' Carlton's voice arrested John before he could move out of the bedroom. 'I will talk with her during the next few days. It's not your fault, and you mustn't wear the blame of it.'

John nodded imperceptibly, though he wondered if the reverend had seen it in the dim light.

'Take all the time you need, John. I will do my best to get better. It will all work out well in the finish. You will see.'

John left his sister's house without having a reply to offer. He wished with all his heart that he could believe it would all work out. He saw Kate's bitterness, and though he didn't blame her for it, he didn't think he could live with it either. Every word that had come from her mouth since he'd returned to get her had been a barbed comment that had cut him deep. He had wanted to love her, but she had made that all but impossible. All he could do now was fulfil a promise to her father.

God, will the rest of our lives be this miserable? He asked the question as a prayer. *How can we possibly live together under these conditions?* As the train pulled away from Melbourne, and moved through the peaceful countryside, John felt as if some of the agitation had seeped away. By the time they had approached Brinsford, he thought that there might be hope, with time, just as his father-in-law had encouraged.

Kate didn't quite know what to feel when she discovered that John had left without saying goodbye. She felt hurt by it, and yet she scolded herself for feeling this way. She had no special affection for him, she thought, so why should this action make any difference to her whatsoever? Yet it did. Though she was safe, dry, well fed, and with her father, Kate felt insecure. But to admit that she needed John would be going beyond the boundaries she had set herself, so she tried to chase the thoughts away.

'How are you feeling, Papa?' She asked her father on the morning of their third day.

'I have to confess, I am feeling a lot better. It is a great comfort to me to have you close by, and to know that you are well taken care of. John has done a good thing for you, I hope you realise that.'

'Let's not bring him up now, Papa. Let's just enjoy the time that we have without him.'

Carlton let the comment pass. He decided it would be best just to allow the seed time to take root.

'Do you think you are well enough to come downstairs for a short while?'

'Do you know, I think I will, but not today. Perhaps tomorrow, if I am feeling as well as I do now.'

This news cheered Kate, and her frame of mind improved ever so slightly.

When she met with John's family, downstairs, she was able to conduct herself in a polite and acceptable manner, but she warned herself that it was for her father's sake that she did so. She would not allow that she behaved properly out of respect for her so-called husband.

Sandra was attentive to a fault. She lavished Kate with attention, and Kate found that she had quite grown to liking her sister-in-law, until this morning.

'I don't know . . .' Kate stammered in response to Sandra's news.

'What's not to know, Kate? John didn't have time to take you across town, but the situation has turned in our favour after all. Mother has sent word that she is to visit this afternoon. You will have to meet her sooner or later, you know. She really isn't that formidable. I know you will be able to hold your own with her.' Sandra squeezed Kate's hand for courage.

'You don't understand,' Kate argued meekly. 'It isn't what you think.'

'Oh! Kate. John should never have put those doubts in your mind about Mother not approving. She won't have a choice, now, will she?'

'But . . .'

'Are you worried about that other girl, Bernice?' Sandra hurried on. 'You shouldn't give her a second thought. John doesn't know it, but Bernice will probably elope soon. Of course her father doesn't know. Bernice is a lovely girl, but she didn't love John at all. You don't know what a relief it is to know that my brother has found someone he truly loves. It has been a great relief for me.'

'John doesn't love me!' Kate blurted the words out in a rushed attempt to get them said before Sandra spoke again.

'What? What are you saying?' Sandra's happy, self-assured manner instantly turned to concern.

'Sandra, I'm sorry. You have been so kind to me, I didn't want to burden you with all our problems.'

'I don't understand, Kate. Of course John loves you. I know my own brother.'

'He intends to have our marriage annulled as soon as a more suitable arrangement can be made.'

'Annulled! I don't believe it! Does you father know you're talking like this? Such a shock might kill him!'

'He knows. John proposed marriage to me only to make a way to get my father out of the poorhouse, and me out of Mercy of Heaven home.'

'Kate! No!' Sandra clapped a hand over her mouth which fully indicated her alarm. 'You can't mean that. Surely you haven't . . . who was responsible for putting you in a place like that?'

'John put me there. He left me there when he had promised he would take me to my father.'

'John! John did that to you? No! I won't believe it, Kate. My brother has faults, I know, but he would never compromise a young girl in such a way. And if he did,' she hurried on, 'he would marry her, and not carelessly leave her and his child in a place like that.'

Kate reddened at the comment. 'Sandra, stop! I will have to start again. You have gotten the wrong story completely. It is bad, but not that bad.'

'Then you had better tell me the whole story. I must know the truth now. I cannot believe my brother would do such a thing.'

It took nearly a half hour to relate the whole tragic tale to the sympathetic Sandra. Kate even allowed herself to shed a few tears during part of the telling, but once she had reached the part where she felt John had betrayed and deserted her, her anger returned to colour her tone.

'You can see how I cannot meet your mother. It wouldn't really be fair to her. I already feel bad enough that you have accepted me under false pretences. John really should have told you, but . . . '

'But what? I suppose he thought I would not have taken you in, unless of course you were as close to him as a wife would be.'

'He thought your husband would not approve,' Kate admitted.

'He was quite right. Leonard would not have approved. My charity expression is restricted to monetary contributions through our church. It is not seen as proper for one of my station to be seen in establishments like you have just mentioned.'

'I am so sorry, Sandra. I feel I have imposed on your good graces, and would leave the house instantly if it weren't for my father.'

'Well, you can put all of those thoughts out of your mind, my girl. You won't be going anywhere. John has left you here for me to look after, and look after you, I will!'

'But what about your mother?'

'Never mind your pretty little head about her. You are John's wife, and she will accept you as such.'

'Haven't you heard anything I've said?' Kate sounded frustrated. 'As soon as a suitable alternative can be found, I will not be John's wife.'

'Are you going to look for a suitable alternative?' Sandra asked.

'I wouldn't know where to look,' Kate admitted. 'If I had known before, I would not have lied to your brother in the first place, pretending to be his housekeeper.'

'Well you can go on being his housekeeper, my love, because this marriage will not be annulled.'

'Of course it will. Just as soon as John . . . '

'John will not look for an alternative, Kate. Of that I am certain.'

'Why wouldn't he look? He can't want the burden of us for the rest of his life.'

'Any man who loves a woman as much as John loves you would be happy to have such a burden.'

'That's nonsense!' Kate refused to accept her words. 'He doesn't love me at all.'

'You may think what you want, Kate, but I'm telling you, I know my brother. You would not have seen or heard from him once your housekeeping fraud was discovered, if he didn't love you. John is not one to buy into scandal, unless of course he has lost all sense of reason to a greater emotion. No! It is Mrs Laslett now, and it will always be Mrs Laslett, unless you do what your mother did to your father. I hope you won't, Kate. I really hope that you don't.'

CHAPTER 10

John waited until the last possible moment before he decided he must return to Melbourne. There was no turning back from the decision now. The moment he'd arrived back in Green Valley, the Hodges had drawn the truth from him – every last detail. Together they had formu-lated a version they felt Lady Vera would accept. John informed the grand lady that he had taken a wife, while in Melbourne, and he hoped that she would extend to them, as a couple, her blessing.

'Of course!' Lady Vera sounded pleased enough. 'I've always maintained that having a wife to help in the ministry is the very best of all. Of course, our last minister lost his wife early, but his daughter served very well in her stead, once she was old enough.'

John heard her analysis, and decided to store it away for a time when he knew he would need some back-up support. Lady Vera obviously didn't know that he was aware of the whole saga surrounding the former minister.

As he packed a few clothes for his journey, John thought over the last few weeks he'd spent in the Valley. He had engaged Hodges during his spare time, and together they had weather-proofed the back veranda. John had already decided that his father-in-law would be installed back into his own room. Kate would have her room, and so he did what was necessary to make a comfortable bedroom for himself out the back of the house.

'How long do you think you'll have to stay out here?'
Hodges asked, not unkindly.

'Only as long as it takes Kate to find a better situation
for herself and her father.'

'You don't think she'll be changin' her mind then?' he'd
asked.

'About what?' John sounded confused.

' 'Bout being your wife. Your real wife, I mean.'

John was challenged by the thought, but he didn't
allow himself to dwell on the prospect for too long. He
was certain that if he considered it, he would be completely consumed with the whole idea, and it would
break his heart to eventually let her go.

And so John experienced some anxiety during the trip
to the city. He wondered if the situation had improved
any; if Kate had lessened in her anger toward him; if
Carlton had gained any health. But the only way any of
his questions could be answered was if he actually faced
up to the family staying with his sister.

Kate was surprised when John actually walked into
the drawing room. They had not had any word to expect
him, and so his arrival caught her unguarded. At Sandra's
exclamation of delighted welcome, Kate found herself
offering a smile of pleasure. It annoyed her that she
should be so careless, especially since John saw her smile,
and his own face lit up with animation.

'How is your father, Kate?' he asked without further
delay.

'He is much improved, thanks to your sister's fussing.'
Once again, Kate could not help being vulnerable as she
offered the answer. As John gave instructions to the servant, concerning his luggage, Kate made it her business
to re-erect her wall of indifference. She simply didn't have
the confidence to leave herself emotionally wide open. It

didn't feel safe, and withdrawal seemed the more secure option.

'That is a lovely dress, Kate.' John spoke sincerely. 'I have never seen it on you before. Is it new?'

Kate scolded herself as she found a blush climbing in her cheeks, and was glad to hear her sister-in-law make an answer for her.

'I'm glad you noticed, brother dear,' Sandra began. 'It is a wedding gift to your lovely wife.'

'You didn't have to.' John began to object.

'Oh! But I didn't. Go on Kate! Tell your husband who the gift is from.'

Kate tried not to show her distress. She was fully aware of what Sandra was trying to do. She knew that to her sister-in-law it was only a matter of a few well-placed words, and the two would go flying into each other's arms. But Kate's resolve to withhold far surpassed any of Sandra's ideals.

'Don't be shy, Kate,' Sandra admonished. 'It's Mother's gift to your wife.' Sandra revealed the information with great relish.

'Mother?' John looked astonished. 'What . . . How did she . . .?'

'I introduced your wife to your mother, since you were in so much of a hurry to be away. Oh, and don't look at me like that. It was a job well done.'

'Sandra!' John spoke with forced restraint.

'She didn't fuss for long, John. Kate's pleasant personality soon softened her.'

'Sandra. I need to talk to you – now!' John forced his sister away from his wife, in a half-hearted attempt at privacy.

'Don't go taking the high hand with me, brother. I know all about that supposed temporary scheme you've cooked up. You don't mean a word of it.'

'Sandra! You are interfering in something you don't know anything about.'

'A blind man could see that you love her, John. Why pretend otherwise?'

'Perhaps it is you who are blind!' John's voice had risen in volume. 'You should have left well enough alone. Now you've made things more difficult.'

'Just how is the situation more difficult?' Sandra feigned innocence.

'What am I supposed to tell Mother when Kate finds another place? Oh! Didn't you know?' John's tone showed traces of his own hurt. 'Yes, sister! This young lady here doesn't really love me. She has been forced into this marriage by circumstance, or didn't she tell you?'

'Don't be ridiculous, John! You've had a shaky start but give her a little time.'

'A little time?' John sounded exasperated, recalling all that he'd tried and failed to achieve. 'I fear it's a little late for that. Kate has made it perfectly clear that she despises me.'

'Shh! John. She can hear every word you say.' Sandra became alarmed at his uncharacteristic display of passionate emotion.

'I don't care if she can,' he forged on. 'How many times has she taken the opportunity to let me know in no uncertain terms that she doesn't even like me, let alone trust me? She seems to take great delight in making me feel as if I'm the villain.'

'John! You are making this worse for yourself.' Sandra had converted to a stern tone.

'Nothing could be worse than it already is. As soon as I can, I want Kate to find another place. I can't take any more of the barbed comments, Sandra. I can't bear to have her nearby, knowing that all she feels for me is resentment.'

Sandra looked despairingly across to where Kate had been sitting, and noticed that she had already left the room.

'All of the work I did while you were away, you have just managed to ruin in one moment of unguarded passion. Well done, John! Well done!'

John retreated from the drawing room in a mixture of emotion. He had already begun to berate himself for having spoken so harshly – and yet it had seemed almost to well up out of nowhere, as if the hurt he felt had a mind of its own.

'Welcome back, John.' Carlton's tone of greeting was warm and almost strong. John would have been pleased if he had not been so mixed up in his thoughts. The only reason he had gone to Carlton's room was because he had nowhere else to retreat from the situation downstairs.

'What is the matter, son?' Carlton had discerned immediately that he was upset. 'Has Kate spoken harshly to you again and so soon? I'm sorry, John. I really thought that your sister had managed to win her over.'

'It was me, this time,' John confessed mournfully. 'I lashed out at her, and without any real reason.'

'I don't understand.' Carlton seemed genuinely confused.

'It's stupid, isn't it? I have recited to myself, over and over, all of the things I could lecture her on concerning bitterness, and all the time I have been no different. All the time I have been away, I have been busily building up a wall of protection around my heart. A wall that doesn't just shut new pain out, but shuts the old pain in. And now I just let it pour out without restraint.' He sighed in regret. 'It's hopeless, isn't it, sir?'

'No, son! It is difficult, but it is not hopeless!'

'Don't try to change my mind, please,' Kate was crying as she spoke to Sandra. 'You had almost convinced me, and I had nearly let my guard down. But I'm glad I didn't.'

'Kate! I'm sorry. John was just confused. He didn't mean . . .'

'I heard what he said, Sandra. I know you mean well, but you can't go on pretending. This is a temporary arrangement, and the sooner I find somewhere else to go, the better it will be for all of us.'

Sandra was stuck for words. She was certain that her brother and his wife could make a happy couple, if only they would stop misunderstanding each other. But in all of her 'interfering' she had never come across such a stalemate as she now experienced. She didn't know which way to pursue now. Sitting down on the bed, next to Kate, she began to stroke her hair. 'I'm sorry, love. I don't want to see you hurt. I don't want to see either of you hurt.'

'Then help me find a way to break this relationship, once and for all.'

'I wish you would give it more time,' Sandra sighed, almost defeated.

'Would you let us stay here with you? I know it's a lot to ask,' Kate hurried on, 'but it would be so much easier if I didn't have to go with him back to Green Valley.'

Sandra thought on the request for a moment, before answering. 'No, Kate! I won't let you stay here. I see your pain, and I see John's pain, but I am still convinced that you could work it out, if only you gave it a chance. No! I will not keep you here so that you can find another man.'

'I don't want another man!' Kate cried out frustrated.

'How else do you expect to set yourself up, my girl? Your father is too ill to support you in any way. And it would be the next thing to adultery for you to marry someone else.'

'Sandra!' Kate sounded shocked.

'Well it would be!' Sandra held to her statement. 'John is your husband. He loves you, and wants to look after you. I will not be the one to stand in his way.'

Kate turned away from her sister-in-law annoyed and somewhat defeated. 'You refuse to see reason,' she accused softly. 'Even when he said it plainly, downstairs, you still refuse to accept it.'

'It is you who refuses to see, my love.' Sandra spoke comfortingly. 'The pair of you, I do declare, are both being as stubborn as Balaam's donkey!'

Sandra's behaviour analysis was performed down to the last detail during the train trip home. Kate stubbornly nursed her grievance; John stubbornly refused to attempt any more peace-making manoeuvres.

Carlton's physical health had improved enough for the trip to be of little effect on him. He silently observed his daughter and son-in-law as they skirted every issue of relationship. He wanted very much to take a firm hand with Kate, and insist that she see sense, but he knew that parental interference would not be the best tonic. He wisely decided to refrain from comment, and instead committed the unhappy marriage to the Lord in prayer.

Kate didn't know whether to be pleased or put out at seeing Mr Hodges waiting on the platform at Brinsford. It was apparent that he had made arrangements to meet them, and convey them back to the manse in Green Valley.

'Reverend Winston!' Hodges seemed genuinely pleased to welcome his former minister and friend. 'It's so good to have you back with us again.'

'Does Lady Wallace know?' Carlton was quick to remind them all of the trouble he had caused.

'No, my friend. Not yet. We thought it'd be best to let you settle awhile, before we sought her approval.'

'And if she doesn't approve?'

'Then we'll cross that bridge when we come to it.' Hodges seemed willing to let the matter rest there. As if he wanted to make that clear, he turned his attention to the young people, waiting patiently behind.

'Reverend Laslett! Welcome home. And Mrs Laslett,' he focused on Kate's blushing face. 'Congratulations! M'wife and I couldn't be more pleased to hear of ye marriage.' Hodges kissed Kate's hand, and gave her a warm smile. 'Come along,' he directed. 'Let's not be wastin' any time gettin' you settled in your home.'

Kate didn't know how to respond. She knew how rude and childish it would have been for her to react to the words spoken, and yet she was furious that Hodges had already known.

'How many people in the Valley know about us?' Kate whispered angrily, once they began to move along.

'Don't worry yourself,' John bit back. 'Hodges knows the rules. He won't have told anyone else. You'll still be free to go the minute the notion takes you.'

Kate settled back, wondering why she should feel guilty. It was the arrangement they had agreed upon, after all. *Bothersome man*, she thought. *Why is it that he makes me feel like a brattish child?*

As the buggy drew closer to the manse, Kate listened as John began to address her father.

'Hodges and I have spent some time fixing up the back. We've made quite a comfortable bedroom out of the veranda.'

'How could you?' Kate was instantly on the attack. 'My father has been so ill, and now you just want to toss him outside to sleep, like so much extra baggage.'

'I don't intend to put your father outside . . .'

'Well, if it's me you intend to leave out there, it won't matter. I'm used to the freezing cold of the store shed anyway.'

John raised his eyebrows in frustration and turned his gaze out the side, to stare aimlessly at the passing countryside.

'Katie!' Carlton spoke in a low tone, and threw a disapproving glare her way.

'What?' She reacted violently. 'He doesn't want us here any more than I want to be here.'

Carlton also shook his head in resignation. Kate had been absolutely impossible since John had returned to fetch them home. She was difficult to get on with, and waspish in her tone. Both men fought with ideas of what they could do to bring her out of her present mood.

Finally, the manse came into view, and Hodges pulled the horses up outside the front door.

'Are y' going to carry your bride across the threshold?' Hodges asked the question, fully aware of the mischief he was making, but he pretended innocence anyway. He looked questioningly at the pair, as if he dared them to tell him the truth.

'Mr Hodges . . .' John began to make excuse.

'Oh! Don't go bein' embarrassed on my account. Reverend Winston and I'll move out of the way quick smart, and leave you alone for your special moment.'

Hodges knew exactly what he was doing, and he encouraged the senior reverend to follow his cheeky lead. He picked up one of the trunks and moved toward the front door. 'You've the key, Reverend Winston. Could you be so kind as to open the door for us?'

As the two older gentlemen disappeared inside, John turned a miserable face toward his 'bride'. 'Well! What impression is it that I'm supposed to give, Kate? Do you want Hodges to think we are a happy couple, or would you prefer he knew that we can't stand the sight of each other?'

'You're supposed to be the head of the house, sir. What do you want him to believe?' Kate had no intention of going along with Hodges. She only wanted to throw another sharp comment.

As if it were the straw that broke the camel's back, John moved aggressively toward her. 'I want him to believe that we are properly married!' He issued the remark as he swept her off her feet and conducted her over the threshold and into the house. Kate hardly had time to register the action before he'd dumped her unceremoniously in the passage entrance. 'There you are, Mrs Laslett.' He spoke in a low, yet angry tone. 'Welcome home!'

Kate was dumbfounded as she watched her husband walk into the main bedroom.

'Already going to lock himself away, I suppose,' she accused under her breath.

But as she walked down the hallway, she had reason to stop and look into the room – the room that had been her sick room.

'How are you feeling, after your trip, sir?' she heard John kindly inquire.

'I'm not too bad, considering all that bumping and jostling about.'

Kate walked into the room to see her father seated in the window chair, a lap rug already covering his knees. John was kneeling down at the fireplace, coaxing the laid kindling into flame. She had only to look about the room to see that all of John's things had been removed, and now her father's small trunk sat unopened by the bed.

'I trust that you will be comfortable here.'

'I should be, son,' Carlton reassured. 'This was my room for the best part of twenty years.'

'I know! I'm sorry you ever had to be moved out of it.'

Kate withdrew silently from the room. She felt shame, yet again, for having unjustly accused her husband of thoughtlessly throwing her father out the back. She moved cautiously down to the back bedroom to find out the whole truth. Her regret felt like a lump of clay in her stomach as she saw her own things ready, waiting to be unpacked.

She didn't have to look at the new room outside to know what John had done, but she ventured there anyway. Just as she had recently suspected, all of John's personal belongings had been placed neatly around the small, lean-to chamber.

'I wasn't going to make you sleep out here, either, you know.' John's voice startled Kate from her thoughts.

'I'm sorry, John. I was unfair to you.' Kate kept her head down and gaze averted from him. The apology had cost her a lot of pride, though she knew it would have cost her more not to make it. After a few strained moments, when neither had made any comment nor any move, John eventually spoke. 'Do you think you could make your father some tea? He will need some refreshment before he retires for the night.'

CHAPTER 11

*L*ife at the manse had settled into a satisfactory routine. It was not so good that the head of the house
and his wife actually spoke to one another, but at
least the work schedules were accepted and fulfilled. John
had asked Kate if she wanted him to employ a housekeeper, to which she had given a nasty answer.

'What do you think I am, if I'm not a housekeeper?'

John didn't bother to ask again. The way he'd been
brought up, he had always expected that he would provide house help for his family. It had always been that
way when he'd been a child, and he felt that it was his
responsibility now. But Kate's attitude was such that John
doubted his ideals.

In fact, John had begun to doubt everything. He had
gone back to his habit of allowing Lady Wallace to tell
him what she wanted preached, and whom she expected
he would visit. All of his hard learned lessons during the
tough months – the instruction in the ways of conviction
– had fallen away. John had lost his sense of confidence
that had been building. He didn't seem to care, any more,
whether he acted with authority or not. It simply didn't
matter.

Kate noticed his apathy, and instantly condemned him
for it. She thought of all the faithful people of Green
Valley – the ones who were not welcomed into the church
services – and she burned with anger. Her father asked
after each one, but she had nothing to report. Carlton was

not well enough to minister to them, and Kate felt she must remain a recluse in the Valley. She hoped that Hodges had not told others of her presence there. She did not want to have people expecting her to fulfil a role that she hoped to abandon as quickly as possible.

'Why don't you and John visit the Browning family?' Carlton asked his daughter, as she poured out his tea one afternoon.

'John? Visit one of the poor families? You must be joking, Papa. John wouldn't be caught dead within a stone's throw of one of them. It would be beneath his high and mighty upbringing.'

'Katie!' Carlton cast aside his decision not to meddle. 'You are too hard on your husband.'

'He is not my husband, Papa.'

'What is he to you, then?' he asked, patience straining in his tone.

'The same as he is to you. He is our only hope of survival, but he's only doing it out of a guilty conscience!'

'Katie. I wish you would stop your slanderous talk. None of what you say is true. Just look around you, child. You are in your own home, your own bed. You have food and clothes provided. He even wants to give you a housemaid to ease your burden.'

'How do you know that?' Kate's eyes lit up with accusation.

'He told me.'

'He would!' Kate's tone was moody. 'I suppose he wanted to impress you with how generous he was.'

'No! He was worried that he was not doing the right thing by you. He asked me if I thought it was improper to be letting you do all the work on your own.'

'And what did you tell him?'

'I told him that you were behaving like a spoiled child, and if I were him, I would have taken you over my knee by now.'

'Papa!' Kate sounded shocked.

'Yes I would have, Katie. I'm ashamed of the way you have been behaving.'

'You make it sound as if I were the one who caused all of this trouble.'

'Initially, it was my fault, and John made one or two mistakes, yes, but lately, it is you who is making life in the manse a pure hell.'

Kate stood aghast, her mouth open in shock. 'You can't mean that?' She tried to maintain her proud tone.

'I can, and I do, child. I have never seen such a display of wilful childishness in all my born days.'

'If that were so, why haven't you said something before this?' She tried to sound as if she had gained back some ground in defence.

'Because, my dear, it is no longer my responsibility. I am no longer the head of this household. John is your husband, and he should have taken a firm hand here.'

'But we agreed!' Kate was losing confidence. 'This is only a temporary arrangement. Just as soon as we find another place, we can have the marriage annulled.'

'No, Katie! There won't be any annulment.'

'But, why not? You agreed.'

'I agreed because it was the only way to get you to the altar.'

'But Papa, why would you want me to marry a man I don't love? Why would you want me to be unhappy? We could find another place, just as soon as you get well.'

'You don't understand, do you child?' Carlton lessened the force in his voice. 'I've known it from the first, and John's known for a long time too.'

'Known what?' Kate sounded alarmed.

'I won't be getting well, Katie. I'm living on borrowed time now. I don't know how long it will be, but I know that my time is running out.'

Kate was astounded at what she was hearing, and at first she didn't want to hear it. She covered her hands over her ears and shook her head as if this action could change what he was saying. But after some minutes, when she looked back at him, and saw him still staring mournfully at her, she knew that the truth was here to haunt her. Her father was dying, and there was nothing she could do to stop it.

'But what about me, Papa? Don't leave me all alone. How will I manage?' She fell on her knees and buried her head in his lap, hiding the tears that were coursing down her cheeks.

'You are not alone, Katie.' He spoke gently as he stroked her hair. 'I've found a husband for you, or at least, he has found us. And he will be a good husband, Katie. John is a good man. He just needs a little encouragement, instead of continual criticism. Can't you see that?'

Kate couldn't see it, and she didn't want to see it. She didn't want to see anything, save her own sorrow. Why did her father have to be dying? Why did he have to leave her? Teatime forgotten, Kate stayed with her father, crying her anguish out as he comforted and reassured.

'Please give John a chance, little one,' Carlton eventually asked, some hour later. 'The two of you could be happy, I know it. If only you will give him a chance.'

Kate didn't want to deny her father anything now, even though she felt like blurting out her refusal to cooperate. But with the news that he might soon be gone, she was aware that she must present a different image. He had called her childish and badly behaved. He had surmised that she had been making life hell for all of them. These opinions stung Kate's pride, but she knew it would be foolish to continue denying the truth of them. Later, as she thought over the afternoon's conversation, she had to admit that what her father had said was true. She had been hard to get on with in every way. *God, help me to improve my attitude*, she prayed before drifting off to sleep. *I want my father to be proud of me in his last days.*

John had noticed the change in his housekeeper/wife's attitude. She still did not talk to him, but she had stopped being openly critical, and didn't take every opportunity to attack his character. He wondered what had brought about the change, but he didn't dare ask.

'Lady Wallace has been asking about meeting my wife.' John made the comment in conversation with Carlton one morning.

'What excuse have you given?' The older man seemed concerned.

'I told her, quite truthfully, that my wife was unwilling to leave her father just yet. I explained just how ill you have been.'

'So she knows I am back in the Valley, then?'

'She knows my father-in-law is living with me at the manse, but she refers to you only as Mrs Laslett's poor father.'

'Kate has not visited anyone in the district, has she?'

'No! But I know she wants to get back out amongst the poor families. It must be a battle for her. She doesn't want anyone to know she's back – she wants to sneak out as soon as she can. Still, she can hardly bear the thought of all her friends so close, and her being unable to visit.'

'Has she spoken to you about this?'

'Kate doesn't speak to me about anything, sir. But I can see it in her eyes.'

'I've told her there isn't going to be any annulment.' Carlton threw the information in with ease.

'What? What do you mean? Do you know how she will react if she thinks I won't let her have her freedom?'

'She knows I'm dying, son. There won't be any freedom for her outside of the manse. If you are still willing to have her, I beg of you to take care of her as your wife.'

'It's not a matter of whether I will have her,' John argued. 'It's more a matter of whether she will have me. I want to introduce her to Lady Wallace, and to the parish, but I have to confess, I'm afraid to ask her.'

'Don't ask her, John. Tell her.'

John stared back at the older man, incredulous at what he just heard. 'You can't mean that I should order her to do something she doesn't want to do.'

'John, John. You must learn about authority in the home. I'm not asking you to become a tyrant, though I doubt that you could, ever, even if you tried. All I'm saying is, you must make Kate understand what is the best for her. If she refuses to see sense, then you will have to take a firm stand. You must know what is the best for your family. She is not a stupid girl – only stubborn. I have brought her up to know the difference between right and wrong, and she will see the right of it.'

'But what if she . . .'

'If she argues with you; belittles you; refuses you. John, you are afraid of her emotional tantrums, and you are making it worse by letting her get away with it. I'm afraid you've been used to letting this happen in your life before.'

'You mean with my mother?'

'And Lady Wallace. You're afraid to stand up to her too, aren't you?'

'It's not easy,' John confessed.

'But don't you see? Half of Kate's problem is that she thinks she doesn't respect you. Every woman wants a husband she can respect. She needs to know that you will lead her and her children safely and wisely. She needs to know that you will stand up for your convictions without fear; that you can't be manipulated by emotional blackmail.'

'But that is what she is doing to me.'

'Then you must stop her.'

'You make it sound very simple. I don't want to hurt her, you know.'

'You are letting her hurt herself. She is so caught up with her past hurts that she is almost incapable of making a sound decision. If you love her, and if you want to win her respect, you must lead her with strength of character. Do you understand me, John?'

'I understand you, sir, but I don't feel very confident.'

'Practice will make perfect, my boy. Practice.'

<hr/>

'Practice makes perfect,' John mumbled to himself later that afternoon, just before he sought Kate's attention.

'Kate!' He swallowed the lump of apprehension in his throat as he called her name.

She heard him, and turned in his direction, fighting all of her desire to be wilful and childish.

'I have arranged for us to take morning tea with Lady Vera, tomorrow. If that is not suitable for you, then I will send word to make the appointment for the day after.'

Kate wanted to shout out a thousand different refusals, but each one got tangled up with the other, and in the end nothing came out.

'Which day would you prefer?' John bravely pushed for an answer.

'Are you saying I have no choice in the matter?' Finally, Kate's mind snapped to a violent attention.

'Yes, you have a choice. Would you prefer tomorrow, or the day after?'

'What if I don't want to take tea with Lady Vera?'

'Think for a moment, Kate. We often have to do things we don't want to do. But we usually do the things that are necessary and right – even the distasteful things. Lady Vera has asked to meet you, and I don't think it is right to put her off any longer. Do you?'

Kate was momentarily lost for words at John's sudden clarity of thought and strength of will.

'Perhaps you would like some time to think about it,' he offered. 'I will need to send word before dinner, if you could let me know before then.' With that said, John turned and walked out of the room, before his resolve crumbled. Though his heart hammered madly, and sweat had broken out on his brow, he felt proud of himself, and hoped Kate would respond positively.

Kate didn't wait too long before she sought the counsel of her father. 'Now he is ordering me what to do!' she complained bitterly.

'Has he asked you to do something wrong or immoral?' Carlton didn't let her know that he was already abreast of what was going on.

'Is it immoral to visit Lady Wallace? Sometimes I think it is!'

'Don't talk nonsense, child,' Carlton rebuked.

'She has treated us very badly, Papa. I don't suppose John has thought what the good lady might think, knowing that we are both back in the manse.'

'I think you need to trust John, and give him a chance to work out this difficult situation.'

'Trust him! Why?'

'Has he ever given you any reason to think he might harm you?'

'What about the time he left . . .'

'We're not going to bring up the Mercy of Heaven incident again, are we?' Carlton's tone revealed strained patience.

'Well?'

'He had no other choice, did he, Kate?'

Kate was unwilling to admit the truth of it. It was her only defence against having to trust him.

'Just try it, child. He won't hurt you, I promise.'

Carlton's perseverance and caring attitude was more than Kate could fight against, so she quickly left the room. 'Dinner will be in half an hour.' She threw the needless comment over her shoulder as she walked out.

Later that evening, as the three sat around the dinner table, John brought up the subject again. 'I'm sorry, Kate. I haven't sent any word to change tomorrow's appointment. I take it that tomorrow suits you.'

'No! Tomorrow doesn't suit me, neither does the next day, or the next. I have no wish to take tea with the woman who has brought about so much misery in my life.'

'I know. I understand.' John's answer was caring and patient.

Kate settled down from her agitated state, thinking she had won, but was soon revived when she heard her husband continue.

'Will you be all right for an hour or two, sir, when your daughter and I go to visit Lady Wallace?'

Before Carlton could get out his reply, Kate had cut in. 'I thought I told you I didn't want to visit Lady Wallace.'

'You did mention it.' John remained calm. 'I understand your misgivings, but we must go nevertheless.'

'You can't make me go!' Kate was bordering on rebellion.

'I won't drag you there kicking and screaming, if that's what you mean, but I am politely asking you to consider what is right, and to trust my judgement in this matter.'

Kate looked to her father for support, but Carlton wisely turned his head away from the conflict.

'I would appreciate your cooperation, Kate. The issue with Lady Wallace needs to be confronted, and I feel that now is the time to do it. I will support you, you needn't worry about that. You are my wife, and I will stand up for you.'

There was nothing else Kate could say. She couldn't refute the logic of the argument, for to do so would be being openly rebellious for rebellion's sake. She found herself in a position whereby she was forced to comply. Her own sense of reason told her that.

CHAPTER 12

Kate was in a dark mood when she woke the next morning. She was fully aware of what was expected of her, and she was tempted to throw a colourful display of temper, enough to relieve her of the obligation. But to her dismay, she found a small part of her conscience still existed, and challenged her about her attitude. To defy John on this issue would be justified only by her own selfishness. The only other excuse was her fear of confrontation, but John had made it quite clear that he intended to face the supposed 'evil', and deal with it once and for all. He had spoken with more confidence and assurance on this point than Kate had ever heard him use before. Some unidentified emotion lurched in her stomach as she thought of his self-assurance.

'What am I supposed to wear?' She grumbled to herself, in an attempt to ward off any unwanted tender feelings. 'She already thinks I'm a tramp, what difference is making myself up going to make?'

Even as she argued with herself, Kate still fussed and preened. It was at this point she regretted having left her mother-in-law's wedding gift with Sandra. It had been pride that made her refuse to bring it along to Green Valley. She had been so certain that she would be cut adrift from the Laslett family by now, that she would not have been ever able to wear the dress. But here she was, engaged to be introduced officially as the minister's wife, and now was the moment when the dress would have been just the thing she needed. Kate growled under her breath again, wanting to cast blame in her husband's direction, but she was finding it more and more difficult to do so, since her father's candid discussion on her behaviour. By the time mid-morning had arrived, Kate had done her best, considering her mood, to make herself presentable for someone so important.

'You look lovely, this morning,' Carlton observed proudly, the moment she walked in, 'doesn't she, John?'

John had no wish to disagree, but he didn't know just how much he dare reveal. That he was completely mesmerised by her appearance was a fact he felt he needed to conceal. He managed a nod of assent, hoping that his thoughts were not too apparent on his face. He was a little annoyed at himself for having let his emotions wander into regions previously forbidden. When he'd left Melbourne, he had declared to himself that he would not allow himself to be so enraptured with this woman, but here he was acknowledging dangerous feelings.

'If you are ready, Kate, we will need to be getting along.'

Kate kissed her father lightly on the cheek, before following John as he made his way out of the front door. 'Will you be all right, while I'm away?' she asked kindly, an amount of doubtful concern in her voice.

'Go along, Katie,' he ordered gently. 'Just seeing the two of you together is medicine enough for the day.'

Kate allowed a smile to escape her defences. She quickly retreated, afraid that her father might see it and make more of it than she intended.

Hodges had been sent to pick the couple up, and Kate was saved from having to make any comment during the ride, as John was kept occupied in conversation with the driver. Kate had been to the Wallace mansion on several occasions, mostly to accompany her father on official business. Today, however, her stomach knotted with anxiety at the thought of what Lady Vera would say. She had no illusions as to what the Lady was like. Even with a proper marriage to hide behind, Kate doubted that Lady Wallace would be willing to forgive her lies, or her father's lie. She fretted inwardly, knowing that there had been no real excuse to lie. Perhaps if she had presented her desperate case to John the moment he'd arrived, he would have assisted her in a way that would have been acceptable to all concerned.

But there was little to be gained by past regrets now. She had made a choice in a moment of distress, and that choice had yielded nothing but trouble. Now she was to face the one woman who could, if she so chose, release Kate from the self-recrimination and guilt that constantly plagued her mind. John had forgiven her, so had the Hodges. But she knew, until she had Lady Vera's pardon, she would feel responsible for any difficulties that might beset John, as the minister, because of her.

'Are you all right?' John's compassionate question broke into Kate's introspection. 'If it weren't so important to get this matter cleared up, I would not put you through all this.'

Kate wanted to melt in his sympathy, but didn't feel she had the right to be taking so much support from someone she had treated so badly.

'I will be all right,' she eventually answered, trying to set his mind at ease, even while trying to put out her own fires of doubt. As if he read her apprehension, John took her hand and increased the pressure. Kate didn't know which way to look, and she had no more words to add. It was only the fact that they were approaching the mansion that she was able to turn her thoughts to another course.

'Could you inform Lady Wallace that Reverend and Mrs Laslett have arrived?' Hodges issued this request to the doorman, before turning back to assist the young lady from the carriage. 'You do look a vision today, Mrs Laslett,' Hodges remarked, a distinct mischief twinkling in his eyes. 'You must be quite proud, Reverend.'

Kate was fuming at the driver. She knew he had always in the past, called her Kate or Katie, and she saw also that he was deliberately baiting John for a compliment.

'Don't make fun of me today,' Kate scolded the older man. 'I have too much to be concerned with, when Lady Vera finds out who I really am.'

'Don't you worry, child,' Hodges reassured. 'Your good man won't let any harm come to you. No harm at all.'

As Kate was shown through the spacious hall, into the grand drawing room, she wished she had Hodges' confidence. She wished she could know with certainty that John would not let any harm come to her. How many battles had she been forced to fight alone? How many claims of innocence had she struggled to maintain? And in all of it, John had been branded as her accomplice, not her protector. If he truly meant what he said, now was the moment to prove himself, for Kate knew that Lady Vera would show little mercy toward her.

Even as they approached the large, double doors, John moved closer to his wife, and tucked her arm protectively in his. It was as if he had read her apprehension, and now sought to chase her fears away.

'Reverend Laslett!' Lady Vera's commanding tone enveloped them the moment they stepped through the door. Kate waited for her Ladyship's gaze to rest on her, and then for her recognition. Her body became tense with anticipation. John felt her physical reaction, and increased his own hold, as if to add confidence.

'Thank you for inviting us, Lady Wallace,' John spoke without fear. 'May I have the pleasure of introducing my wife to you? Kate Laslett, this is Lady Vera Wallace.'

Time seemed suspended for Kate, as she waited for the atmosphere to explode, and when it did, she began to tremble with intimidation.

'I know who she is.' Lady Vera's air had instantly transformed to one of derision. 'What do you mean by bringing somebody like her into my house?'

'I beg your pardon,' John's own muscles became taut as his defences rose. 'You have invited us in good faith, and I am disappointed that you should start to abuse us without reason.'

'Without reason!' Lady Vera exploded. 'Surely Hodges told you what manner of woman this is, Reverend?'

'This young lady is my wife,' John almost shouted back. 'I know of no reason why you should be treating her this way.'

'Because she and her father have both lied. Deceivers, Reverend. But of course you have been taken in by their crafty ways.'

'I am not prepared to stay here, if you persist in this verbal attack.' John's emphasis in low tone could not be mistaken. 'I am perfectly aware of the mistakes my father-in-law has made. I am also aware of the desperate circumstances that were forced upon my wife, and her attempts to survive through them. If lies were told, then I have forgiven them. It is the Word of God, madam. There is no excuse to hold on to this grudge when both Reverend Winston and his daughter have acknowledged their fault, and their desire to be restored. It is now your responsibility to forgive.'

'I have made my decision where Mr Winston is concerned, and I have no desire to be restored to him

whatsoever. As to his daughter's desperate circumstances, it is upon his head. He is the one who created the
lie in the first place, he must be held accountable for her.
Winston was removed from his office because of his weak
moral character. I feel it was to the benefit of the people.
If you persist in this manner, I will have to consider your
fitness for office as well.'

'By all means, consider it,' John challenged. 'I have no
fear of God, for I know that I have conducted myself in an
upright manner. In the places where I have failed, and
where my wife has failed, we have worked to set things
in their proper order.'

'Things are not that easily repaired, in my opinion.' The
older woman refused to soften her attitude. 'Once a liar,
always a liar. You would do well to be on your guard, sir.'

'Good morning, Lady Wallace.' John barely gave the
required parting words, as he almost dragged Kate from
the room.

Terrorised and ashamed, Kate allowed herself to be
pulled through the hallway and down the front steps.
Hodges looked up, surprised to see them emerge from
the visit so soon.

'Please take us home,' John barked angrily. Kate was
more frightened by his current anger than she had been
by the expected reception she'd received indoors. A tense
silence hung over the carriage as Hodges drove them the
two miles back to the manse. Kate noticed John's breath
coming in heavy gasps. She chanced a study of his face,
and saw the intense anger that sparked from his eyes.
Never, in all her time with him, had she seen such a display of intense emotion. Her own fear and distress paled
in significance against that of her husband.

'I'm afraid that you have angered Lady Wallace,' Kate
bravely offered her opinion, once the manse was in sight.

'I said nothing I regret.' John was still tied up in his strong feeling, and didn't appear to notice Kate at all. By the time they reached the manse, John leaped out of the carriage, and walked quickly away toward the church. Kate watched with remorse, sorry that she had not been able to bring some sense of comfort to him. Hodges came around to help her down.

'Don't worry none, Katie. John needed to face the dragon. He needed to stand up to her, or he would have always been under her control. Leave him be, and he will work it through.'

Kate nodded sadly.

'Will you be all right?' Hodges inquired kindly, as he walked her to the front door.

'I hope so, Mr Hodges.' Her voice betrayed her sorrow. 'It's all my fault though, you know. All my fault.'

'It's not so much as you think,' Hodges patted her arm. 'That young minister knew what he was doing when he decided to up and marry you. He knew right back then that he was willing to pay the price necessary to have you as his wife.'

'Do you think that's true?' Kate sounded uncertain. 'I always assumed he was just doing his Christian duty. That he felt obliged.'

'Then you assumed wrong, little lady. You assumed wrong.'

Once inside, Kate ran straight to her father, fell on her knees next to him and buried her head in his lap.

'It had to be done, you understand?' Carlton didn't bother to ask her for details. He was fairly certain he knew how the exchange had taken place. 'I take it John stood up for you. He didn't leave you to be carved up by her words, did he?'

Kate shook her head, but couldn't get any words out over the lump in her throat.

'Do you believe me now, about John I mean? Are you beginning to see that he is not the weak character you always thought?' She nodded. 'He might have had a bad start on his road to conviction, but I am almost certain that he will make a dynamic man of God before the pair of you are finished. You will stay with him and help him succeed, won't you Katie?' Once again Kate nodded. She felt so foolish and so sorry for the way she had misjudged, and the way she had mistreated him. Now that she had begun to allow a little, the whole truth seemed to flood in to condemn her.

'How will he ever forgive me?' Kate eventually asked her father. 'Will he ever know that I have changed, or will he always keep clear of me?'

'You just be open and honest, Katie, and don't let any of that bitterness come back to deceive you. It won't be long and the two of you will break down this intolerable barrier that has been between you. It won't be long now.'

CHAPTER 13

❦

Kate had gone to bed that night, still quite upset. John had not returned by dinnertime, and she felt sure he must have been regretting having ever taken her in. It was entirely possible that they would *all* be left homeless now, if Lady Wallace could think of an appropriate title to put to John's offence. Kate allowed the dinner to be overdone for half an hour before she had gone out into the twilight to search for her husband. Carlton had encouraged her to go, though she had objected at first. 'It's quite obvious that he is angry with me. Why else would he stay out for so long?' Kate had argued.

'Go out and find him, Kate. Let him know that you are no longer angry with him, at least.'

But when Kate eventually did find her husband, she did not have the courage to tell him anything. 'Are you coming in for dinner?' she asked tentatively.

'I'm not hungry!' His tone was sullen. 'You eat with your father. I'm not finished here yet.'

Kate could not think what it was he wasn't finished with as she looked around the cold church. He had been there the best part of the day, and apart from the Bible in his hands, she could see nothing else that could be occupying his time. Still she was in no frame of mind to argue, so she left him alone.

She had seen that her father was safe in bed before she retired for the night, and still there had been no sign of John. Kate fretted and worried. All of a sudden, the blame she had so easily thrown at him, she now heaped upon her own head. Her defences were no longer in place to filter out warm emotions. They were there in full force, taunting her, especially now that there was no way for them to be fulfilled.

Kate could not go to sleep until she heard John return to the house through the back door. And even then, her rest was fitful and restless.

When she found herself wide awake, sometime before dawn, Kate lay still and began to reason with herself. *It isn't any use my sulking and worrying*, she rationalised. *It is as Papa says. I will have to help him succeed. All the rest will take time. I must give it time.* And so with this new resolve, Kate began to make plans.

No sooner had she served and cleaned up from breakfast, than she decided to put her plans into action. She told her father, briefly, of her idea, kissed him goodbye and left the manse. By the time John came in search of her, she had been gone for over an hour.

'Do you know where Kate has gone?' he asked Carlton. 'I can't seem to find her anywhere.'

'Isn't she back yet?' Carlton sounded confused.

'Back from where?' John asked.

'I thought you knew. I thought she had discussed this idea with you.'

'What idea?'

'Oh! She's a troublesome girl, that one!' Carlton wasn't really as cross as he sounded. 'She has gone out visiting, John.'

'Visiting? Yesterday was the first time she has been out of the manse since we've been back. Who would she have gone to visit?'

'You will have to talk to her,' Carlton advised. 'I didn't know that you were unaware, or I would not have let her go so easily.'

'That was what I planned to do – talk to her. I was so angry yesterday, I don't think I offered her a civil word. I wanted to apologise, and to see if she was all right. It must have been so hard for her to hear all of that.'

'Your sentiments are good, son, but a little ill-timed, I'm afraid. She could have used some reassurance last night.'

'I suppose she is angry with me again.' He sounded resigned to that fact already.

'Not at all. No! I think she may have finally seen the truth about you. That's why she has gotten about her business so early this morning.'

'Just what business is she up to, sir?' John asked, half amused, half afraid.

'She has gone to represent you to the poorer families. All of those people who form the church outside of the church.'

'Represent me?' He seemed alarmed.

'My understanding is that she intends to offer the ministry we both used to offer, but in your name – that is to say, as a representative of yours.'

'Why didn't she ask me?' John knew it was hardly fair to be interrogating the father, when it was the daughter he wanted answers from.

'My guess is, she was afraid you wouldn't want anything to do with those outside the recognised parish.'

'That's silly!' John sounded disgusted. 'She only had to talk to me about it. It's not like I'm an ogre or anything – am I?' He suddenly wondered if his recent stand of authority might have been over the acceptable limit.

'No, John! You are not anything like an ogre, though I think you might have shaken her up with your anger yesterday. Why don't you go out and join her in the visit. You can sort out the facts of the matter later on.'

John took Carlton's advice, and also his hunch as to which family he thought Kate might be with. He saddled his horse and urged it into a canter, suddenly in a hurry to 'set the record straight'.

Carlton's hunch proved near to the mark. Kate had been to the Brownings, but had not stayed long, as Mrs Browning informed him. There had been a tragedy with the Shore family, further along the Valley, and Kate had hurried over there to offer her support. John thanked the woman, and expressed his hope that he might visit properly with them in the near future.

'Thank you, Reverend,' Mrs Browning smiled. 'I am glad that Kate has found a kind and honest husband. She is a good, hard-working girl. Now I can see that the Lord has blessed her.'

John smiled to himself as he rode away from the Browning farm. *If only we could really be husband and wife*, he thought to himself. *She is a good and hard-working girl, but I'm fast reaching the conclusion that this is not enough.*

John slowed his horse to a respectful walk as he approached the ramshackle cabin that must have been the Shores' place. He dismounted and tied the horse to a tree, some yards away from the front door. There were several children playing out the front of the house, all of them poorly clad, and most wearing the day's dirt. 'Is this the Shores' house?' he asked one of the older girls.

'Yes, sir,' the child answered sadly. 'My mum's inside with the minister's wife. They're both crying. My dad was killed last week, and my mum hasn't stopped crying since. Don't reckon she knows what to do now.'

John's heart went out to the child, and he knelt down so that he could look directly into her face. 'Don't you worry too much, missy,' he began. 'We will do what we can to make sure you're all looked after.'

The child gave him a weak smile. 'I hope so, mister. I'm so hungry. So is the baby.'

John left the child then, and moved toward the house. He didn't want to frighten the grieving widow, so he waited outside, listening for a moment, to ascertain the right move to make next.

'My oldest boy, Colin, has dug him a grave, and we buried him last Saturday.' Mrs Shore broke up with weeping. 'We didn't have no money to pay for a coffin or nothin' fancy. He's just out there, lying in the ground with nothin' said over him. No prayers offered.'

'I'm so sorry, Mrs Shore,' Kate tried to comfort her. 'If only I'd known.'

'What could've you done, missy? Your father's been drummed out of the district, and by all accounts, that new minister is as pumped full of himself as Lady Wallace herself.'

'Reverend Laslett is not as selfish as Lady Wallace,' Kate argued. 'He has come to my rescue on several occasions. I'm sure he wouldn't object if I were to come and pray over your husband's grave.'

'Do you think you could?' Mrs Shore sounded hopeful.

'Perhaps, if my father is feeling well, he might even come and pay his respects,' Kate offered hopefully.

'Wouldn't it be grand if the new minister himself were to come? We could have a proper funeral for my poor man.'

'I will do what I can, Mrs Shore,' Kate promised, 'but I can't promise you that. Reverend Laslett was brought up in the higher classes, you see. I don't know if he would . . .' Before Kate could finish her excuse, she was arrested by a light knocking at the door.

'Mercy!' The distressed woman cried. 'Who could that be?'

Kate quieted the woman before going to answer the door. But her own agitation was to increase when she saw her husband standing there, a look of displeasure on his face.

'Pardon my intrusion, madam,' John addressed the widow, 'but I would like a few words with my wife, if I may.'

Kate's heart sank as she realised John must have heard the recent conversation. She felt that he must have been absolutely furious with her. 'Excuse me, Mrs Shore.' Kate leaned near her and spoke quietly. 'I won't be a few moments.'

Once outside, Kate waited quietly for the wrath to come. 'How could you?' John began abruptly.

'The poor woman needs someone to look out for her,' Kate defended. 'I didn't think you would mind if I came.'

'I don't mean that,' he said, obviously frustrated. 'How could you misrepresent me like that?'

'Like what?' Kate was astounded. 'I knew you would-n't want anything to do with these people, but I didn't think you would object to my still caring for them.'

'You cannot mean that?' John was incredulous. 'You have never once spoken to me about these people. You cannot possibly have any idea of what I think on the matter.'

'You are from the better classes . . .' She began to point out the obvious.

'So you think I wouldn't be prepared to conduct a funeral for a poor family. What's wrong with you, Kate? What sort of cold-hearted creature do you think I am?'

Kate didn't have any ready reply. She really didn't know John's heart at all, but she was beginning to see that the idea she did have was far from the truth.

'If you are going to go about ministering to people, you should let me know about it first.'

'Don't you trust me?' Kate allowed the bitter comment to come from her lips.

'No! I don't. Not after what I just heard. You make it sound as if I *were* pumped full of myself, Kate. How on earth do you think I can get people to trust me if you let them think such foolishness?'

'Well! You are! Aren't you?' She was back accusing. 'Lady Vera has never approved of Papa doing anything for these people. She would just as soon that they failed and moved out of the district.'

'Even if that is the truth, Kate, what makes you think I am the same as her in my convictions?'

'Because you let her tell you what is and isn't acceptable.'

'Now is not the time to go into it!' John cut her off, no less displeased. 'I want you to do what you can about feeding these children, and I will talk to Mrs Shore about arranging a funeral service for her husband.'

Kate watched, amazed, as John strode away from her, and knocked lightly on the cabin door. She was totally confused about what to think. For months now, she had convinced herself that John was selfish, apathetic and uncaring. Even with Sandra and her father trying to convince her that John was in love with her, she still believed he was inconsiderate about those who were beneath him. She had gradually begun to subscribe to the idea that he would do anything for her because he loved her, but to suddenly consider that he actually had a compassionate and generous nature was almost too much to accept in one session.

When Kate walked back into the cabin, she found John seated with the grieving widow, offering kind words of sympathy. She didn't dare interrupt, and so she quietly moved toward the larder, in search of ingredients she might make into a nourishing meal.

'Would you like a few days to get word to your friends
and neighbours, before we have the service?' John asked
gently. 'If you like, my wife and I can get messages to
those you want informed.' Mrs Shore nodded her head
thankfully, wiping at another tear.

'Do you need us to send someone over to help you for
a few days? Kate could come down, if you wanted her.'

'No! Thank you Reverend.' Mrs Shore found her voice.
'I will be able to manage the house, I think. Just knowing
that my poor man will be properly buried is a great burden off my mind.'

'What about your land, ma'am? Have you thought
what you will do, now that Mr Shore is gone on?'

'My eldest boy, Colin, will have to make a go of it. If he
can't, then we are all lost. We haven't got anywhere else
we can go from here. All of our money is tied up in this
piece of land.'

'How old is Colin?' John asked, concerned.

'He'll be sixteen next birthday. He can do the work of a
man, I'm sure, but he's so young to be takin' on the
responsibility of a whole family to support. I just wish I
could help him in some way.'

John talked more with the woman, allowing her to
share her fears and worries, and offering words of
encouragement where he could. Kate listened, touched
and proud of the way John handled the tragic situation.
By the time she had prepared a basic meal, and had called
the six children in to eat, there was a great deal of calm in
the cabin. John had prayed with the mother, and now
asked if he may pray with the children. Before the minister and his wife left the farm, John asked Colin if he needed anything in the way of help. Though the boy made no
immediate request, John made him promise that he
would send word if he thought he could be of use.

'Let me help you on the horse.' John didn't leave any room for Kate to object.

'What about you?' she asked.

'I can walk!' He seemed unconcerned.

'I can walk too.' She wasn't so much trying to outdo him as she was ashamed to make him walk when she was riding.

'Kate! Do you have to argue with everything I say?' John sounded tired and frustrated.

'I'm sorry, John.' She sounded genuinely repentant. 'I just didn't think it was fair for me to ride, when you had to walk. We have a number of houses to deliver the message to.'

'If you don't mind, then, we can both ride. I will drop you back to the manse, and then I will convey the message around.'

'But . . .' Kate pulled herself up just in time, realising that she was about to argue again.

'But what?' John tried not to sound impatient.

'But you don't know where any of the people live. I do!'

'That is true!' John conceded. 'Very well. We will both ride until I think the poor horse has had enough, and then we will both walk home. We can finish the messages tomorrow.'

Having agreed to the logic, Kate was then faced with the practical outworking of the arrangement. She had not had the advantage of horse riding lessons when she was a child. Her father had been given a horse, just as John had, but she had never ridden alone. She had always sat side-saddle across her father's knee. It seemed that if she were to succeed in the agreement, she would now have to ride side-saddle across her husband's knee. John helped her up, and she held the reins steady while he mounted behind her. She didn't know what to feel when he reached his arms around her to take control of the reins. She was very close to him, so that she could feel his warm breath on the back of her neck. As a final line of defence, she sat stiffly erect and uncomfortable.

'For heaven's sake, Kate!' John eventually complained. 'I am not going to eat you. Why won't you relax a little?'

Kate swallowed hard. She could hardly explain why it was that she couldn't relax. What was she supposed to say to him? I can't let myself melt into your arms because . . . Because why? She had no suitable answer.

'Do you think it's proper?' she finally asked.

'Do you want me to walk?' he countered.

'No! That would be silly.'

'So is this!'

Gradually, Kate forced herself to relax, leaning back against his chest. At first she felt like she wanted to jump off the horse and run as fast as she could, away from the feelings that assailed her. But after a while, having stayed put, she began to forget all about whether it was proper or not, and she began to enjoy the ride, breathing deeply of the fresh afternoon air.

'Kate!' John broke the peaceful silence that had enveloped them for the last fifteen minutes.

'Yes. What is it?' She became re-alert to his closeness.

'I was proud of the way you ministered to those people back there. You did a very good job.'

Kate smiled with pleasure at his approval. 'I was proud of what you did, too. I never knew that you had such a tender side.'

'There are a lot of things you don't know about me,' he murmured, content to let the magic moment continue.

'Perhaps you will teach me, soon.'

'Perhaps.'

CHAPTER 14

❧⚜❧

Kate couldn't help reliving those enchanting moments she had experienced during the ride around the farms. She would never have confessed it for the world, but she longed for the physical closeness that riding double had afforded. But the following days, John asked Hodges if he would allow them the use of one of the small buggies to finish the job of visiting the Shores' neighbours. Remembering the sharp complaints her backside made, after having sat for so long over the front of a saddle, Kate had to acknowledge that taking the buggy was a far better idea. Still, she wondered if John had felt any pleasure at being so close, or if it had meant nothing to him, and he was just as happy to revert to their familiar distance. With these doubts nagging, Kate determined that she would not think on the issue again, and went along on the errand, resolved to be on her best behaviour.

The night before the funeral service, the family at the manse sat around the drawing room fire, discussing all that had transpired over the past few days.

'I think I will come with you, tomorrow.' Carlton made the comment in a casual manner.

'Papa!' Kate instantly objected. 'You are not well enough yet. You shouldn't move from here.'

'Please, Katie!' Carlton held his own. 'I wish you would understand. I am not expecting to ever be well again. I have decided to do what I can, while the good Lord still grants me life. I was the Shores' minister for years. I think I should make an effort to be at the funeral.'

Kate tried to restrain the moisture that would form in her eyes, and she recognised that it would be fruitless to make further argument on the matter.

'I don't understand some things,' John changed the subject. 'Why is Lady Wallace so antagonistic towards the small land-holders?'

Kate knew the question had come about because of something Hodges had said earlier in the day. The burly man had given them the use of the buggy, but had shown some reluctance, citing that he was sure his employer would be unhappy if she knew what they were using it for.

'It's not really her fault, in one way,' Carlton explained. 'You see, Lady Vera was brought up in the old way of thinking. Her husband brought her out from England shortly after they were married, some twenty-eight years ago. Lord Wallace was from one of the noble families in England, yet his marriage to Lady Vera was, in fact, a step down for her. He was only a lord, but she had ancestry that is said to have included a duke and a prince. Of course things have been changing in the class system in England for years, but Lady Vera holds fiercely to the old ways.

'In her childhood, she saw all the land about was owned and managed by her father. He owned the village; he owned the church; he owned the businesses. His land was farmed by tenant farmers, and they paid him rent at the end of each season. When Lady Wallace migrated out to Australia, she did not really have the blessing of her father. Still, she was determined to prove to him that she could have every advantage and privilege he had provided during childhood, and that she would own and control an estate that rivalled his.

'Lord Wallace was not nearly as ambitious as his wife, but he did what he could to provide her with a grand house and land. Sadly, her husband died tragically early. They never had any children. But Lady Vera was not willing to go back to England in defeat. She had made her vow to prove her ability to her father and she was determined to succeed. Up until the time of her husband's death, they had engaged a minister to conduct services for the staff of the estate. Those early services were held at the big house, in the small chapel they had there. This manse was built for that minister, long before the church was erected.

'I was the second minister to be engaged by the Wallaces and I came only a year before His Lordship passed on. Lady Wallace was grieved, of course, but more fiercely determined than ever to succeed. She built the Green Valley church in memory of her husband.'

'But what about her attitude toward the small farmers?' John was still puzzled, despite the long account.

'Lady Wallace finds it very difficult to accept that any one outside of the noble families can own land. Most of these people have left tenancies or labouring jobs in England, and have grasped this opportunity to make a permanent life of their own. For someone of a lower class to own land doesn't sit well with Lady Vera. She is of the opinion that they should know their place, and stay there. She has made it quite clear that she will not assist them in any way.

'Personally, I think she has harboured hopes of buying up all of the land, and renting it out to tenants. But this is Australia. Things are different here to how they are in England. If there's one thing that these poor farmers have, it's a chance to carve out something better for themselves and their families. In my opinion, Lady Wallace will never discourage them from that purpose, no matter how she opposes them.'

'But she shows benevolence to her employees, and to the business men and women of the town.' John remained bewildered.

'Her employees have kept their station in life, and don't try to rise above it. Lady Wallace believes that her Christian duty is to support them as employees. As for the small businessmen, she was the one who sponsored them to set up in Green Valley. She patronises them, and expects that they pay her the proper amount of respect in return.'

'There is a lot of pride in her, isn't there?' Kate made the comment.

'Yes, Katie! Pride that has been sown in her from her childhood.'

'But that pride has made her do some cruel things. That can't be right, can it?' Kate was seeking to justify her own hurt.

'It's not right in the eyes of the Lord, Katie,' her father explained, 'but it is only what she has been taught. It is our reaction to that cruelty that may eventually help her see what true love and charity is all about. Don't forget that it is not ours to avenge. Ours is to forgive and let the light of Christ's love shine through our lives.'

Kate felt the heaviness of her father's message. She knew that she had failed to allow Christ's love to influence her during her hurt. When she considered it, she had to admit that she had been in error as much as the lady she sought to condemn.

The day that had been set aside for the funeral service was thankfully clear and sunny. It was late autumn, and

Kate knew that they could have just as easily had overcast and wet weather. Now, considering the gathering in honour of Charles Shore was to be held around the gravesite, Kate offered a prayer of thanks for the stable weather conditions.

Carlton had overcome his physical weakness, and allowed John to help him to a seat by the graveside. Together, John and Carlton spoke words of comfort and commitment over the grave, and to the surviving family. Kate stood with Mrs Shore, and put arms of comfort about her as she sobbed out her anguish.

After the small crowd had offered their words of condolence they filtered quietly away. Nearly everyone had left some small gift of food for the family. With everyone else gone, Kate found herself alone with the widow and her children. John had left to take Carlton back to the manse, and had told her he would return to pick her up later.

'It was a beautiful service,' Mrs Shore commented mournfully. 'When Charles was first killed, I thought I would never be able to lift my head again. Oh, I know there are many hard times in front of me and the children, but I have taken courage from today. Your husband is a fine minister, not unlike your father.'

Kate thought on the comparison for a moment, having not considered it before, and she found that John did have many qualities that she had always admired in her father. It was just another fact that had deepened her attraction to him.

Kate stayed with Mrs Shore for several hours, helping her put away the donated groceries, and spending some time preparing some bread and pies. By the time the cabin was in good order and the children had been fed and settled, Kate wondered why her husband had not returned.

'I don't know what could have been keeping him.' She wondered aloud.

'I thought I heard Colin say that your husband was going to come and help him fix something outside,' Mrs Shore answered.

Kate was surprised that she had missed that piece of information. 'Do you mind if I go outside to see if he's there?'

'Not at all. You've done enough here today. I can't thank you enough, Kate.'

As Kate wandered outside in the late afternoon, she wondered why on earth she had pushed John away at the beginning. All the grievances she'd held had begun to lose their strength, and she felt that they were of little importance to her now.

After having searched around the farm for a few minutes, she found Colin and John. She saw them a little way off and could see that John was offering some encouragement to the sorrowing boy. She didn't want to interrupt the serious moment, and so she stood back and studied the scene. It was apparent that the two of them had been mending a fence. The tools stood, leaning against the newly repaired section, as testimony to the labour done.

Inside the pen, Kate saw the milk cow, feeding on freshly tossed hay. It was a picture of peaceful accomplishment, and it made Kate smile.

John had not wanted to pursue the boy's sorrow. He knew that Colin would not want to appear a child, especially now that he was the man of the house. So John had offered to help repair the cow yard, and had worked silently, speaking only those words necessary to get the job done. When the task was complete, and the cow released back into her pen, John decided to take the smallest chance.

'You will miss your father, Colin,' he ventured, 'but I know he would be very proud of the way you have handled the situation so far.'

It only took these words to break down the façade that the fifteen-year-old had desperately tried to hold in place. John was not alarmed when he saw the lad break down in convulsive sobs. He knew that Colin would need his chance to grieve, every bit as much as his mother would, and it was better done now than harbouring the sorrow inside for years to come.

'It's all right to cry, Colin,' John reassured him. 'In fact, it is the best thing to do today – the day you've committed your father to God's mercy. The Bible tells us that there are times to grieve as well as times to rejoice.'

'But Mum will think I'm still a baby. She won't feel secure if I don't stand up and be a man.'

'Whoever told you that a man can't cry?' John asked. 'Perhaps we are not as emotionally expressive as our mothers and sisters, but crying is something that even Jesus did on occasion. When there is great sadness, like you have had this last week, no one would expect you to pretend it didn't hurt. Losing a loved one always hurts, and grieving is God's way of helping us wash that hurt from our soul.'

John continued to offer encouragement and counsel to the boy. They talked of the types of things Colin could expect, now that he was responsible for the family. John volunteered his counsel and help any time Colin felt he needed male support, and the boy responded with relief and gratitude.

Kate had not actually heard the words that had been exchanged in the conversation, but she could tell when

the two of them had finished talking. She saw John smile
and ruffle the boy's hair. Colin yielded a tentative smile in
return. Then they stood and began to walk back towards
the cabin. It was then that John noticed her standing, not
too far away.

'Are you ready to go home, Kate?' he called across the
distance.

'If you think there is nothing more we can do for the
day.'

John looked to his walking companion in question.
'Thanks, Reverend Laslett!' Colin spoke as confidently as
he could. 'I sure do appreciate your giving me a hand
with the fence, but I think we can make it on our own for
the time being at least.'

The buggy ride home was taut with some kind of
tension that Kate found hard to identify. She knew that
neither of them was angry and there was nothing immediately pressing that should have been a worry.
Eventually she decided that she would initiate a conversation, thinking that perhaps it was just the silence that
was strange after so much activity.

'Mrs Shore was very grateful for the service today,' she
began. When John made no immediate comment, Kate
continued. 'She felt it beautiful, the way you and Papa
interacted to commit her husband to the Lord. In fact, she
made the comment that she felt you were a lot like Papa.'

'Your father is a far more godly man than I could ever
hope to be,' John contributed his opinion.

'Maybe!' Kate sounded uncertain. 'But your nature is
not unlike his.'

'I have changed a lot since your father has been at the
manse, Kate. His wisdom and counsel have added so
much to my own understanding. I feel horrified to think
what I would still be if it weren't for his influence.'

'Do you think you have changed that much?' Kate asked.

'You once said to me that I was blind to anyone outside the walls of the Wallace estate. You were right, Kate. I had no idea about the hard-working folk, who fought for every day of existence. My own life has only ever been one of idleness and indulgence. My mother insisted that we have every thing given to us, like being fed with a silver spoon.'

'But now that you've opened your eyes, you are so willing to reach out. You are so compassionate.'

John gave a half smile of irony.

'And I've changed too.' Kate sounded as if she were trying to convince him. 'I have!'

'How so, dear Kate?' John was amused by her insistence.

'I've learned just how prejudiced I could be against people, like yourself – people who have never had the opportunity to know what it is like to live in hardship. I automatically judged you, and concluded that it was due to a faulty character, rather than a faulty education.'

'It's funny isn't it? I was naïve, and you were prejudiced. And now what are we?'

'We are married,' Kate prompted. 'I'm glad that you married me, John.'

'There's only one problem with that.' John drew the horses to a standstill as he spoke, and then turned to capture her complete attention.

'Do you mean you would still want an annulment?' Kate's tone revealed her fear that he might.

'No, Kate! No! The problem is that we are not really married.'

'I signed a piece of paper in a registry office. It was a legal document, as far as I understood.'

'You know what I mean,' he countered. 'You were angry when we took our vows. If you were honest, you would have to confess that you didn't mean a word of what you were forced to say.'

'You're right!' she admitted softly. 'But I regret it now.'

'I'm kind of glad to hear that, in a way,' John confessed softly, leaving the reigns and taking hold of her hands. 'I've wanted to do this for a long time, you know.'

'Do what?' Kate's mouth had dried up with nervous anticipation.

'I'm going to ask you if you would marry me – properly, I mean.'

Bolts of exhilaration shot through Kate, as she understood what he was proposing. 'John! Do you think we could?'

'I won't be happy until we are married in a church, and make our vows before God.'

'But we couldn't do that now,' Kate objected half-heartedly. 'Imagine the scandal it would cause if folk saw us getting married now, especially with us having lived together for all this while.'

'Do you really think I care two bits about scandal? The only thing I have really been able to think about for weeks is how I would finally be able to talk you into it.'

Kate stared at him, amazed at what she was hearing, and so overjoyed that she was mesmerised.

'Will you do it, Kate? Will you marry me properly? Is it a lost cause, or is there some hope that I might actually talk you into it?'

'A lost cause!' Kate exclaimed, alarmed. 'It is what I want more than anything in the world.'

John grinned in relief, and took a step further by drawing his 'wife' into a firm embrace. 'I don't think you would have said "yes" a while ago,' he said in a low voice, with just a hint of mischief. 'I think you would have been happier to disown me altogether.'

'A while ago I was hurt and angry. But my father has spoken sternly to me, and made me see some home truths.' Kate turned her face up to look in his eyes as she spoke. 'And never underestimate the work that your sister Sandra did. She was determined to convince me that you had loved me all along.'

'Neither my sister nor your father have any idea just how much or how long I have loved you. Kate, if you hadn't said yes today, I don't know what I would have done. To have you so near me every day has almost been enough to make me crazy, and yet I knew I couldn't send you away. That would have been worse!'

'I don't want to go away.' Kate responded dreamily, snuggling closer into his arms. 'I want to stay here with you.'

CHAPTER 15

***

Kate could hardly contain her nervous agitation. 'Oh, Sandra! Do you think we are doing the right thing?'

Her sister-in-law paused from her brushing and pinning, a frown fixed firmly on her face. 'Don't tell me you have called me all the way out to the middle of nowhere, and put me through all of this preparation just so you can change your mind.' She sounded disgusted. 'Kate, I thought that you had finally accepted the fact that John loves you. I understood that you might actually love him too!'

'Stop, Sandra. You've misunderstood me again,' Kate laughed. 'Nothing could stop me from marrying John – properly, I mean. What I'm worried about is all of this pomp and ceremony.'

'Pomp and ceremony!' Sandra sounded scandalised. 'Do you call having a small wedding party of six people and a wedding breakfast in the manse, pomp and ceremony? My dear girl. If my mother had just an inkling of what was being passed as her son's formal wedding, she would probably take a fainting spell. As it is, poor Mother has had to come to grips with the fact that her dear boy was married in a registry office, and to a penniless parson's daughter. It has been a bitter pill for her to swallow. If she thought for a moment that there might have been opportunity to organise the biggest social wedding of the year, what we are about to do would pale in significance. This holds no resemblance to pomp and ceremony.'

Kate smiled at her sister-in-law's dramatic protest. 'It just seems . . . almost dishonest.'

'Hold it right there, young lady.' Sandra put the brush down, and placed her hands on her hips. 'Will I have no peace until we have announced the truth to the whole community? Perhaps you would like to have all of your friends and neighbours come to the wedding. I can see it now. "Come one, come all, and see your respectable minister wed the woman he has been living with for the past seven months."' Sandra's voice rang out in mock proclamation.

'You know it was all legal, Sandra,' Kate defended. 'You make it sound more sinful than it really was.'

'Well, either you want the entire district to witness the ceremony, or you want us to go along as we've planned.'

'It would be too confusing to try and explain the whole complicated story now. We had better proceed as planned.'

'Good!' Sandra sounded satisfied, and picked up the brush to continue her efforts at styling the bride's hair.

'You make this seem so easy,' Kate commented, a few moments later, as she watched Sandra's skilled hands shape the curls.

'What?' Sandra seemed determined to be bossy.

'You can make my hair look so . . . so . . . beautiful. I can only ever pin it in a tidy bun at the back of my head.'

'Don't you know I have always dreamed of doing this?' Sandra smiled mischievously. 'I have had to practice in secret, you know. It took me such a long time to bribe the maids into actually showing me what to do, and they made me swear that I would not let my mother know. They were so scared that she would find out that her well-bred daughter actually had a brush in her hand.'

'We've come from such different worlds, Sandra. Do you think that John will be able to accept the difference in me? You know that I am used to all manner of domestic duty.'

'I think he will try to change you, and try to spoil you, as our mother did us. But the two of you will have to come to some form of compromise. Openness and honesty are wonderful tools to happiness in a marriage. You will need to talk about these issues, and find something that both of you are happy to accept.'

'I'm finding it hard enough to accept these.' Kate lifted the satin folds of her wedding gown.

'What? An old rag like that? It's nothing!'

'It might be nothing to you, but I have only ever seen something so extravagant on the likes of Lady Wallace. I never dreamed that I would ever have cause to wear satin and pearls.'

'You fuss too much.' Sandra dismissed the thought. 'You are lucky I only bought the two dresses. Believe me, I was tempted to buy more.'

'Oh, thank goodness you didn't. Where on earth would I have worn such a creation?'

'On your visits to Lady Wallace, of course!' Sandra sounded as if she had it all worked out in her mind.

'Lady Wallace!' Kate almost laughed. She found she could do that now that she had begun to forgive. 'I'm afraid that grand lady is still trying to find a way to relieve John of his position. She feels that his marrying me is a betrayal to her trust and confidence.'

'Oh, pshaw! You just give it time, my girl. The grand lady herself will come begging for your company before her life is out. You wait and see if it's not true.'

Kate laughed, convinced that Sandra was having a joke at her expense.

'Now come along,' Sandra commanded, once she'd executed her finishing touches. 'I want you at that altar before these blossoms begin to wilt.'

Kate couldn't help those misgivings she'd expressed to Sandra. Having Hodges thoroughly check the surrounding landscape, just to make sure the coast was clear, made it seem exactly like they were about to do something dishonest.

'It's all clear, Katie,' he informed her, as he stepped forward to take her arm. 'Your father and groom are all set in the church. Mrs Hodges has given us the signal, and it's time for us to be makin' our grand entrance.'

Kate's stomach did a backward flip, and she looked to her matron of honour for confidence.

'Go on!' Sandra urged. 'You'll have John in a panic if you delay too long.'

Kate moved across the churchyard, supported by her escort and followed by her attendant. Together, the small party moved up the aisle of the church. Kate would have been amused to see Mrs Hodges dab at a stray tear in her eye, but as it was no one noticed Mrs Hodges. John was totally mesmerised by the vision of beauty his bride presented; Kate was too focused on reaching her groom's side.

'Thank you, Hodges,' Carlton released his friend from his duty. 'You have done me a grand service, conducting my daughter to this place for me.' Hodges nodded in acknowledgement, aware that the father could never have walked the distance to the church on his own, let alone supported the bride. As it was, Carlton took the place of the officiating minister, though he had to remain seated at the altar. Hodges quietly retreated, as previously agreed, to take his stand at the door. They had discussed the plan they would employ should any uninvited guests show their curiosity as to the day's events.

'We are gathered here today,' Carlton pushed for all his energy to speak, 'in the sight of God and these witnesses, to join together this man and this woman in holy matrimony.'

At that point, Kate joined Sandra and Mrs Hodges as she allowed tears to form in her eyes. What a joy it was, to realise the love and security that this union promised. John noticed the silver tracks the tears made as they flowed down her cheeks, but didn't make any comment. He only squeezed her hand firmer, more determined than ever to fulfil his part of the sacred vows made.

By the time Carlton had come to the part in the ceremony where the bride and groom were to exchange vows, he was almost breathless. Nonetheless, he proceeded. Over and above the concern Kate had for her father's condition, she concentrated hard on the words she repeated as a pledge. She was only too aware of what she had felt the last time the two of them had stood in this position. She remembered her own mutinous thoughts of that time, and determined she would set the record and her own conscience to rights. So much had changed since that fateful day in the registry office, and Kate was only too willing to thank God that John had not given up on her during her bitter times.

'Will you, Kathryn Elizabeth Winston, take this man, John Edward Laslett, to be your lawful wedded husband; to love, honour and obey; to have and to hold; from this day forward until death do you part?'

Kate listened carefully to each promise, and consented in her heart before answering, 'I will!'

As Carlton pronounced them man and wife, and issued the instruction that John may now kiss his bride, Kate flushed with the fullness of what she felt. She did not hesitate in responding to John's initiative, and in keeping with her resolve to set every issue straight, she took the opportunity to whisper in his ear. 'You have kept every promise to me, my love. I trust you with my very life.'

There had been some loud discussion over the issue, and now it seemed that Kate was to get her own way. But in many regards she was sorry that it was to be so. Sandra had insisted that she would take Carlton to stay a few days with the Hodges. She had declared firmly that she would take every care of the invalid, and that she would be perfectly happy staying with the Hodges. She had been so certain that Carlton's health would stand the change of location, and adamantly stated that she wanted those arrangements to be made.

'It's your wedding, John,' she appealed to her brother. 'It's bad enough that you can't take your wife on a wedding tour, without having all of your in-laws under your feet.'

John was inclined to agree with his sister, but at the same time understood his wife's argument.

'Papa is not well enough to be going any distance. As it is, he has suffered from the exertion of the wedding. I won't feel easy not knowing if he's all right.'

In the end, it was Hodges who put an end to the argument. 'As much as we'd be happy to oblige you in this matter, Mrs Allenby,' he addressed Sandra, 'I'm a-thinkin' it might not be all that wise.'

'How so?' Sandra asked, not quite ready to give up her cause.

'We've played a pretty trick on all the Valley folk, and that's for sure – staging a wedding right under their noses with out one of them so much as having an idea. But . . .'

'But?' John prompted.

'I'm afraid if Carlton comes home with us, he might not be able to leave us for some time, and I'll have a devil of a time tryin' to explain why he was with us in the first place. Everyone knows that the senior reverend is quite the worse for wear. No one would understand his sudden need to visit with old friends. Not a'tall.'

And so, the choice had been made. The six of them who made up the wedding party celebrated as grandly as they dared, considering the circumstances. Mrs Hodges insisted on presiding over the food and other necessary concerns. Sandra took great delight in telling exaggerated stories of her brother's younger years, and even Carlton was able to add one or two comments that brought a sense of family to the occasion.

Eventually, the Hodges went home. Every domestic detail had been seen to, including the rearrangement of the sleeping quarters. Kate wanted to object on every front, but soon found herself outvoted. Carlton was installed in the spare room, Sandra would not hear of any complaint as she settled herself into the sleep-out chamber, and that left the newlyweds to take up their rightful place in the master bedroom.

Kate's concern over the arrangements gradually gave way to nervousness. But that apprehension lasted only as long as it took to find herself safely encircled by her husband's arms. By that time, the whole world could have been on fire, and she would not have cared.

CHAPTER 16

Those first few glorious days of marriage were marred only by Kate's growing concern for her father's health. It was quite obvious that Carlton had deteriorated considerably. Kate wanted to fret over what she saw, but Sandra was firm in not allowing her to be troubled during her brief, and somewhat cluttered honeymoon.

'I will stay with your father,' she recited over and over. 'I want you and John to go out visiting. I hope you spend more time driving than you actually do visiting,' she whispered as an aside.

Kate could do nothing to dampen her sister-in-law's incurable sense of romance. But then, she did not really want to. If it hadn't been for Sandra's planning and manipulating, Kate knew that she and John would have had a miserable time of worry and anxiety. She knew that the period was all too short before Mrs Allenby would be expected back with her own family.

'Your sister has been so good to me,' Kate shared with her husband, one night as they prepared for bed. 'I will miss her terribly when she goes home.'

'You may.' He seemed unconvinced.

'What do you mean by that?' Kate was surprised at his non-committal attitude.

'Sandra is a dear,' John conceded, 'but she is too much like my mother for me to have her in my home for too long a period of time.'

'But I thought your mother and sister were different.' Kate's confusion was apparent in her tone.

'They are different in a lot of ways, but there is one great similarity. They both love to meddle and to have their own way.'

Kate laughed. She knew the truth of it, though Sandra's meddling had only yielded good fruit so far. 'I will still miss her,' she murmured before drifting off to sleep.

When Kate finally came to saying goodbye to Sandra, she allowed that very thought to be fully expressed. 'You have been such a help to me.' Kate expressed her appreciation over and over again. 'I don't know what we will do without you.'

'I was only thinking that myself.' Sandra took up the thought, as if she were in the middle of a nice long chat, and not just about to leave the manse. 'I cannot understand why John hasn't at least employed some decent house help for you. Why haven't you, John?' She turned the thought into a question and threw it straight to her brother. 'Mother would be absolutely scandalised to know that a Mrs Laslett was forced to do everything for herself.'

'Forced!' John almost choked. 'My Mrs Laslett, forced to do for herself! You've got the story all wrong, Sandra dear. In fact, if you can extract permission from my Mrs Laslett to have another woman in her kitchen, then let me know. I would appreciate that as your good deed for the day. I have been feeling terrible about the situation myself.'

'Oh, stop it!' Kate scolded. 'It is all stuff and nonsense, paying good money to someone else, while I sit about the house doing nothing. Don't you two forget that I have been well used to doing for myself.'

John shrugged his shoulders in resignation. 'I told you,' he glanced at his sister.

'You should think it through a bit more.' Sandra was not quite so willing to let the issue go. 'If you had someone in the kitchen, and even to help in the laundry, you would have more time to spend amongst your parishioners. Just think what it would be like to come home from a day of helping the poor and sick, only to find the dinner already on the table. And then your evening hours could be spent with your father. And when the children come . . .'

'Thank you, Sandra.' John cut her off. 'I promise you, we will discuss the idea some more, if it will set your mind at ease.'

'My mind would be greatly pacified if I knew that you were already resolved to find the right girl for the job by the end of the week.'

'You were right, John.' Kate frowned playfully at her sister-in-law. 'Your sister does meddle too much!'

And so Kate waved goodbye to Sandra, and wiped a tear from her eye as she watched her husband escort his sister away from the manse, and on to the station at Brinsford. She turned back indoors fully aware of the grim atmosphere that was left to keep her company. Carlton had become frail. He'd lost weight to the point of looking gaunt, and his colour was poor. Kate was afraid of what she saw, and tried desperately to look for signs that would promise a return to health.

'How are you now, Papa?' She asked the question, not expecting a particularly rosy answer.

'Much the same as yesterday,' he answered as positively as he could. 'You will miss the energetic spirit that Sandra had with her, Kate,' he observed, quite naturally. 'Pardon me for eavesdropping, daughter, but I think they are right about you having someone else here in the house. Just to keep you company would do as much good as actually helping you.'

'Shame on you, Papa,' she scolded him without feeling. 'You shouldn't be bothering yourself with my domestic worries. You have enough to worry about with your health.'

'I won't always be here for companionship, Katie. You must know that.'

'Oh, Papa! I wish you wouldn't talk about it.'

'You must consider it, child. The time will come, and I will be gone.'

'But why? I don't understand why it has to be so soon. You are not that old. Not old enough for me to be ready to give you up yet, anyway.'

'I don't regret too many things.' Carlton began to reveal his heart. 'I know that I have served the Lord, and my life has had purpose and meaning. There is a little bit of me in many people of the Valley. Just a little bit of hope and love that I have been able to share.'

'It's true!' Kate acknowledged, no matter how much she disliked the way the conversation tilted.

'And I do believe I could hold on to life just long enough to see a little bit of me in flesh and blood.'

'What do you mean?' Kate asked the question, though she thought she knew exactly what he meant.

'A grandchild, Katie.' He held her gaze meaningfully.

'You have been a wonderful child – a delight to call my own, but it has always been a hope that I would one day have a grandson. I knew, once your mother was gone, that I would never have a son to carry on the Winston name. Perhaps you might think it a foolish dream, but I would long to know that a child will be born who could be an heir, if only in name.'

Kate did what she could to change the subject. For days she had tried to provoke her father's interest and enthusiasm, telling him about old friends they'd visited, and the joys and hopes of his former parishioners. But on each occasion he'd hardly responded with more than a tired smile, as if he was glad, but not a part of their life any more.

But now, the subject of a child had come up, and Kate saw the light of eagerness she'd so been trying to engage, only this time she was troubled. It wasn't that she disliked children or even the thought of being a mother herself, more than a realisation that Carlton had one last desire in this life. Perhaps with faulty logic, Kate worried that once he realised this dream, he would simply lie back and let go of this life. She didn't want to face this likelihood. She wanted him to fight and regain his health, though in the back of her mind, she knew he wouldn't.

Kate withdrew from her father and began to sort through her anxieties. *If he hears of his last hope coming to pass, will he perk up, and fight harder,* she asked herself, *or will he take hold of that hope and let go of this life completely?* Kate simply didn't know the answer, and she didn't like what reason told her. To make matters worse, she suspected the much hoped for grandchild might already be on its way.

⁂

As much as Kate hated to admit it, her time spent at Mercy of Heaven home for unwed mothers provided her with all of the information she needed to know about her own condition. She tried not to think of that dreadful time and place, and yet many memories persisted in coming to the fore as her own body began to do exactly as she had learned it must when a woman was with child.

For an event that should have brought her so much joy and anticipation, there was an incredible amount of confusion and worry attached to it. Kate knew that the bad memories were only a part of the distress. The harsh accusations of the sisters during that time had made her resist any symptom that might even be related to a state of pregnancy; for to be pregnant those months ago would have been for her to be at her lowest point of demise. She would never have admitted to it then, and now, that same spirit seemed to haunt her thoughts.

But the other, more powerful objection that stole from Kate's peace of mind was the suspicion that news of a coming child could possibly improve his situation, but was equally as likely to hurry her father's death. It was a silly thought, she recited to herself over and over, but still it prevented her from enjoying the revelation. Some moments she was resolved that she would whisper her good news to her husband. But then the opportunity would arrive, and she was filled with fear again. Just when she'd almost talked herself out of one worry, she thought of a new one. *What if the excitement of the announcement would be too much for him*? The ambivalence had her swinging from one emotion to the next until she made a firm decision. Kate was determined to hold it out to the last, and so she held the truth from everyone.

John did wonder briefly at his wife's sudden compliance to the idea of household help, but credited it to her desire to be more involved with the parish folk. If it hadn't been for Kate's fierce resoluteness, both he and her father would have noticed the subtle changes in her behaviour. Kate's energy levels sagged; her appetite wavered and discriminated where once before it had no favourites; even her moods became more fragile, and while John noticed this, he put it down to the tension that existed knowing her father was dying.

'I think I've found a girl who would suit the position,' John offered this information at the dinner table.

'Oh? Who?' Kate tried to hide the reserve she felt from showing in her tone. She had given in to this idea only because she knew she could not cope alone any longer. Nursing her father had become a monumental task, and added to this was the visiting she would keep up to appear normal. In any other circumstance, she would have fought to keep her kitchen to herself.

'The eldest girl of that family who live up behind the Browning's place,' John answered her question with ease.

'The Smyths?' Kate knew the family and the girl, and would have had no objection if it had not meant swallowing a great deal of pride.

'Yes! Lilly, I think her name is. Lilly Smyth.'

'Isn't she a little young?' Kate asked, knowing that it was a weak excuse, being as Lilly was only three years younger than herself.

'Perhaps,' John answered, 'though even that could go very well in your favour.'

'How do you mean?' Kate was intrigued by his cryptic words.

'She is old enough to be capable. Maybe she hasn't much experience, but that gives you the golden opportunity to teach her how to do things the way you like them to be done.'

Kate had nothing left to do but to agree with John's analysis. She didn't like the idea, but there was no alternative open to her. She had to have help, and she agreed to allow Lilly Smyth the chance to prove herself useful.

It only took John the one day to put the proposal to Mr and Mrs Smyth. Their eldest daughter was seventeen, and long past the age whereby she could have been taken in marriage. It was only the lack of a proposal that kept her in her parents' home.

'I'm sure that the few pennies you could be paying her will be of great benefit to the family,' Mr Smyth issued his strong opinion.

John had taken in the number of children the farmer was supporting, eight in all. He also noted that the four eldest were girls. He knew that the mother had all the help she could ever need, and that the father was accepting the help of his daughters in the field grudgingly. To be in such a position was not at all the way one would have planned it. A man needed his son to add strength and prosperity to a large family. It was only as the minister offered the job to Lilly that the father took any heart in the fact that his daughters could be of any use at all in helping feed the numerous children.

'Our Lilly is a good and sensible girl,' Mrs Smyth seemed intent upon adding her own character reference. 'She's worked hard and without complaint.'

'Aye, sir,' the father nodded, 'and 'tis our hope that she'll not be available to you for long. There's a young man who's been putting some hard work in to get a place of his own. Maybe only a year at most before Lilly will be her own mistress.'

'Perhaps, when that blessed time arrives, one of your other daughters might like to take her place at the manse.' John offered the position freely, trying not to think of what his wife may say in objection. He hoped that she would assent to the idea of having household help, once she'd become used to it.

'You are too generous, Reverend,' Mrs Smyth smiled openly. 'I do hope your wife can afford to have one of our girls to aid her in her time of need.'

'I'm afraid this time, her father being so ill, has been a terrible strain on her. Mrs Laslett has always been strong and resourceful, and it is only now that I'm noticing her lack of health. I don't think it is anything more serious than worry. It is a dreadful time of anticipation. We are all expecting Reverend Winston's time to come sooner or later, but I have to confess, it has provided me with the excuse I need.'

'Excuse? Why would you be needing an excuse?' The farmer seemed confused. John laughed in response.

'My wife and I have been brought up in two different worlds. Hers is one of domestic duty and faithfulness; mine one of idle leisure. I never want her to become as useless as some of the ladies I've grown up amongst, but I do want to provide some help for her, especially when she is so dedicated to working with you, her friends of the Valley. If her energy had not failed, she would never have allowed me to offer Lilly anything but a cup of tea.'

'Have you ever considered, Reverend, that your wife might have something other than worry ailing her?'

Mrs Smyth's innocent question, once considered, sent waves of panic through John's mind. 'I pray not, ma'am,' John sounded shaken. 'Watching her father in his illness has been a strain on all of us. I would not want any disease to be touching my dear Kate.'

'Mercy, no!' Mrs Smyth seemed as alarmed as the good husband. 'I didn't mean that a'tall. There are other things, pardon my language sir, that may ail a wife. It's not fit to be discussin' such things here o' course!'

John grasped her veiled reference, and hurried away from the subject, as decorum would have dictated. But by the time he'd left the farm, he had food for thought. Could his wife be with child? It was entirely possible, he supposed, from his limited knowledge of the condition; but he dismissed the idea easily, citing that she would have surely informed him by now if that had been the case. Still, he congratulated himself on having engaged a housekeeper to begin work at the manse the following day. At least Kate, whatever her ailment, would have someone to ease the burden she bore for the time being.

CHAPTER 17

※ ❧ ❀ ❧ ※

Since the time of the 'real' wedding, neither Kate nor Carlton had been back inside the church building. Carlton lamented the fact often, but his health prevented another such excursion. Kate, on the other hand, made no comment on the matter. She excused herself on the grounds of being needed to nurse her father. John suspected the truth – his theory lying in the realms of her being terrified of facing the intimidating person of Lady Vera Wallace. As it was, that distinguished woman treated her parish minister with a distinctly cold air. She gave him the expected greeting, but never once asked after his wife or his father-in-law. John did not quite feel equal to the task of bringing the matter up to her face.

The Hodges, however, were consistent in their inquiry after the reverend's family, even while being discreet. They hung back, until most of the other respected congregation had given their words of acknowledgment, before moving forward to add their own expressions of concern.

'The senior reverend is not doing well, I take it?' Hodges spoke what he knew to be the truth. 'How is Mrs Laslett coping with it all?'

'She has at last allowed me to employ some help for her. Her own health has not been quite what it has been before, and even she has admitted to needing someone to aid with the upkeep of the house.'

'Perhaps she is in the family way,' Mrs Hodges made the observation casually, and then apologised. 'Sorry to mention it,' she said quickly.

Once again, John considered the idea that had been twice suggested. *But surely she would have said something to me*, he reasoned it away.

And so Kate kept the secret hidden. John might have suspected it, if he had not been so certain that his wife would have informed him of something so wonderful. As it was, he put her ill health down to every other circumstance that was present.

Lilly Smyth came to the manse, and barring Kate's tendency to be a little snappy at first, she did the job to everyone's satisfaction, including Kate's. It was not easy for the mistress of the house to admit that Lilly had eased her burden a great deal, but eventually, she was forced to acknowledge it.

'Thank you again, Lilly,' John offered his gratitude as they watched her prepare to leave for the evening. 'You have been doing a marvellous job. I am so grateful, and I know my wife is too, aren't you Kate?'

'Why, yes.' Kate was caught unguarded, and fumbled for the right words to say. 'I have been a little picky.' She watched, embarrassed, as Lilly smiled at this remark.

'I know how hard it must be for you, Kate.' Lilly was not afraid to use the familiar name, as the two young ladies had been close enough acquaintance for years. 'You could do this job with your eyes shut, and I know it. I'm just grateful to your husband for the opportunity to help put bread on our table at home, and I hope I've been of some use to you while the situation is as it is.'

Kate felt ashamed of herself. 'Thank you, Lilly, for understanding. I'm a silly goose, I know. You are doing a fine job, just as good as I could do. It's my foolish pride

that causes me to be such an old grump. You will forgive
me, I hope?'

'Of course!' Lilly smiled again, and shook her friend's
hand as she went. 'I'll see you all in the morning.'

John felt satisfied that Kate had at last recognised her ill
humour for what it was – foolish pride. He decided not to
make a lecture out of it, but rather to show his affection
by drawing her close in an embrace, once the pair had
gone to bed.

'This job is a real blessing to the Smyths, you know,' he
spoke in a matter-of-fact way, as he buried his face into
her hair.

'I know, John,' Kate answered with a sigh.

'I just want you to know that I'm thankful to you for
allowing it so gracefully.'

'Gracefully!' Kate turned in his arms to face her husband. 'I'm glad you're not angry with me, but you had better not hide the truth from yourself. I have been anything
but graceful about it. Lilly is graceful, yes, but me . . .'

'It doesn't matter.' John seemed prepared to overlook
the fault. 'I'm just glad that you have help, and I hope that
you regain your spark soon.' He paused momentarily,
thinking on what had been suggested to him, and decided to open the matter for discussion. 'You know,' he began
again, 'both Mrs Hodges and Mrs Smyth suggested that
you might not be yourself because you may be expecting
a baby. It's silly, isn't it!' As John made the comment, he
allowed his hand to move over her abdomen, but instead
of it being a caressing gesture, it turned into a moment of
revelation. Kate stiffened as she knew what her husband
must feel. She had been sure of the pregnancy herself for
nearly five months. Even she knew that the secret must
get out soon, and now that it certainly must, she froze
with guilt.

'It's not silly, John,' Kate whispered, ashamed. 'It's the truth of the matter.'

John revealed his hurt by withdrawing slightly from her. 'Why haven't you told me?' he asked, pain evident in his tone. He waited for a few moments, expecting some sort of answer, but when none came, he resolved to pursue it further. 'I can't pretend I'm not upset at your having kept this from me, Kate. I thought we were finished hurting one another.'

Kate wanted to answer, but the shame of having done this to her husband, along with the distress of the real reason why she had, rose up to choke her words from being formed. At that moment, all she wanted was for John to hold her closely, and to understand her grief, but she held back, knowing that he had plenty of reason to be angry.

'Are we going to play that old game of misunderstanding?' Anger coloured the minister's question. 'Why won't you talk to me?' he persisted. 'Have you decided you made a mistake in marrying after all?'

'No, John!' She pushed the denial out over her pent up emotion. 'Please! It's so hard to explain.'

'Would you mind giving it a try? I'm feeling a little cheated at the moment. I had fooled myself into thinking that this marriage had a future after all, but now I'm beginning to doubt my own ability to discern the truth. I have lived under the misapprehension, all these years, that news of an expected baby was an event that warranted much celebration. Correct me if I'm wrong, but I was under the impression that the father usually had the privilege of being deliriously happy.'

Kate could hear the edge of fury in John's words, and it served as a sharp rebuke on top of the grief she felt. She knew that everything he was saying about celebration and anticipation was correct, but she had carefully talked herself out of those ideas in her mind, as she stubbornly clung to the idea that she might be able to prevent her father's leaving them.

'Kate, I'm sorry,' John sounded resolute, 'but I'm not prepared to go back to the old days of drawing apart, and holding back the truth from one another. I want you to tell me what's going on, and I want you to tell me now.'

Kate wanted openness too. In fact, as she heard him speak the words, she wondered why she had not told John the whole of her fears the moment they had risen up in her mind. She hoped that she had not lost the closeness she now knew she needed more than ever. Though John retained some of his ire, he allowed his wife to move into his arms. He held some reserve though, despite her pathetic, tearful state.

'I've been so afraid, John,' Kate allowed the words to mingle with her weeping.

'We must trust God.' John didn't have any other answer to give. He knew the dangers of childbirth, despite being a man. Too many women gave their lives in the attempt to provide their husbands with offspring. It was a consideration, but not one he wanted to think about himself. 'A majority of women have healthy babies,' he quoted, 'and usually fair very well, I've heard.' He recited this information, as much to allay his own fears as hers.

'It's not me I'm afraid for,' Kate replied, somewhat calmed by his misinterpretation.

'What then?' John's tone had gentled considerably.

'It's Papa.'

'I don't understand! Your having a child can have no influence on his health. I believe he would be most pleased to hear of a grandchild. It would be a great kindness to him, particularly since . . .'

'John, don't! I've not been thinking straight, I know, but I just can't face the fact that he will leave us.'

'This has nothing to do with our having a child, Kate, does it?'

'I'm sorry, John. But don't you think that when Papa finds out there will be nothing left for him to live for?'

John paused, at last aware of what had been Kate's mistaken motivation in hiding this news. It became quite clear why she had hidden an otherwise wonderful revelation.

'My little Kathryn,' he rocked her gently as he spoke. 'You can't change God's timing. Your father is ill, and he is convinced that his time on this earth is done. He has no regrets, save one. Not telling him about his grandchild may only serve to not ever allow him that joy. He might have passed from us without ever knowing. You must tell him so that he can rejoice with us, for however long that will be.'

Kate nodded weakly, her tears dampening her husband's nightshirt.

'I'm sorry, John. I've wanted to tell you, I really have, only I was afraid . . . '

'Shh!' John comforted, as he gently cradled her. 'Tomorrow we will tell him, and then we will all celebrate.'

Just as John had decreed, the announcement was made the following day. Kate stood back, half afraid, half ashamed, and not feeling at all like what she would have wished to feel. John, on the other hand, was quite determined to treat his father-in-law as if nothing were amiss. The pride was clearly marked, both on his countenance and in his tone, as he broke the news to Carlton.

'I have wonderful news!' John beamed to the senior gentleman as he walked into his bedroom. 'News that'll have you wanting to get out of that bed and leaping about.'

'I believe we must be due for some good news,' Carlton remarked, already more alert than the previous day.

'Come in here, my darling.' John tugged on Kate's hand, and drew her into the bedroom. 'Carlton!' John began his formal presentation. 'My wife – your daughter, of course – is going to bless the both of us with a baby.'

'A son?' Carlton's imagination was instantly alerted. 'I've always wanted a son.'

'Papa, I . . .' Kate began to object weakly.

'Uh ah! I'm afraid this time it is me who gets to be the father.' John was resolved to be light-hearted. 'This time, you will have to settle for a grandson, or daughter.'

'Of course!' Carlton snapped back to reality. 'Why, this is wonderful news, Katie. I'm so happy for you both.'

'Thank you, Papa.' Kate responded only as she felt John's pressure on her hand.

'Do you think you could be well enough for a celebration dinner, this evening?' John forged ahead. 'You'll have all day to think on getting enough strength.'

'John, I don't know.' Kate was hesitant as she interrupted.

'That's a marvellous idea!' Carlton cut off her objection. 'I feel better already. I'm sure by this evening I'll be almost ready to dance.'

'Very good, sir,' John laughed. 'I shall set Lilly to the task, and perhaps we shall visit with the Hodges. They would not be happy unless they were invited, of course.'

'In the old days, you could easily have asked Lady Vera as well, but I'm not so sure now.'

'Not yet, sir,' John was sombre for just a second, 'but I have every confidence that she will be offering her congratulations before too long. It is certainly something I plan to work on, at any rate.'

'I'm glad to hear it, son,' Carlton murmured. 'I'm glad to hear it!'

Despite Kate's fear of her father's final collapse, she was overtaken by John's supreme effort to move in the opposite spirit of things. His infectious joy soon drove away those lingering worries, as he chose to introduce a festive mood. By the afternoon, Kate couldn't help but smile at his silly antics. When she stopped to think about the way he was acting, she came to the conclusion that it was exactly how she imagined an expectant father should act – perfectly oblivious to any other consideration.

When the Hodges arrived for 'the dinner', John was no less affected by his newfound status. 'Congratulations, my boy,' Mr Hodges offered, pumping the young minister's hand up and down, and himself in a more cheery state than Kate had seen for a long time.

'Now, you two just bide your time,' Mrs Hodges scowled. 'T'ain't time yet to be jiggin' about. There's a lot of hard work for we women to get done a'fore ye can get to the name makin' ceremony.'

'Don't start dampening our enthusiasm, good woman,' Carlton called from his lounge chair. 'We've not had too much cause for jiggin' in a long while. Let us celebrate while we have the chance.'

Tentatively, Kate sat through the meal, watching closely how her father fared with the extra strain. By the time the Hodges had taken their leave, Kate came to the conclusion that the news had indeed bolstered her father's attitude, to the point that he'd taken physical strength from it. Carlton retired in the early evening, tired and short of breath, but it was a far improvement on other recent days, where he'd scarcely had energy to even come from his bed in the first place. Kate took this observation as an encouraging sign, and as the weeks passed, it became apparent that Carlton's health had taken a turn for the better. Kate held on to this as a positive hope for the future.

CHAPTER 18

⚜

When Mrs Hodges found out just how far along Kate was in her pregnancy, she all but moved into the manse, shaking her head and clucking her disapproval.

'How did ye think we was goin' ta be prepared?' she kept asking the expectant mother. 'Four months is hardly time enough to be properly set up. Just think of all the sewin' and knittin' that needs to be done. And that's not considerin' some tiny furniture that'll need to be got ready.'

Kate took all of the good-natured lectures with grace and ease. She knew the truth of it, and would not become disagreeable when she recognised her own fault in the matter.

Kate set herself to the task with as much enthusiasm as her energy allowed. Lilly had now become an indispensable part of the manse household, and Kate didn't even wish to be back in the kitchen or laundry. She had enough work tending to her father, and trying to meet the sewing schedule that Mrs Hodges had demanded. Though John missed her input greatly, they both agreed that a period of confinement had become necessary, and so he went about his pastoral duties alone. Kate also missed her husband's company, and wished for the fresh air that travelling the countryside had afforded.

Gradually, Kate began to let go of the dread that had held her back in her enthusiasm. Her fear that Carlton would simply give up and die, now that he knew of the coming grandchild, did not materialise. As she noticed her father's somewhat stabilised condition, with no apparent relapse, Kate began to be lured into that false sense of security, where one hopes that no evil will ever come to mar the present.

'I don't know how I would have ever managed if you had not come to us, Lilly.' Kate offered the compliment one morning, as the younger woman brought some tea to serve to Kate in her bed.

'You know it has been my pleasure,' Lilly returned. 'Your father's words of wisdom have always brought comfort to my family, and this gift has not lessened at all, despite his illness.'

'He seems so much better, though, don't you think?' Kate sounded hopeful, and ventured to get an agreement.

'He seems stable, but I don't think his health will ever return, Kate. I don't want to alarm you, especially in your condition, but it would be better if you accepted the inevitable, rather than trying to deny it.'

Kate didn't want to hear this piece of advice, and went strangely quiet.

'Do you want to get out of bed?' Lilly asked before withdrawing, 'or do you want to rest some more?'

'I will get up,' Kate answered, trying to manoeuvre her way to the edge of the bed, her swollen abdomen hampering her every effort. 'I must walk around a bit, despite these puffed up ankles. I cannot bear to sit still for a moment longer.'

'How long do you think it will be before the baby arrives?' Lilly asked kindly.

'That doctor from Brinsford said he wouldn't be looking for it until late April. That's still four weeks away, and I think I'm about ready to go crazy.'

'My mother said the same thing, if I remember rightly, when the last two were due.' Lilly smiled at the memory.

'And you'll say it, too, Lilly,' Kate assured, 'when it's your turn.'

'That may not be too far away,' Lilly mentioned, with a starry-eyed look. 'Ned has finished the building of a hut. He's paid the money for the land.'

'What are you waiting for, then?' Kate asked.

'I don't want to leave the manse until I'm sure you are well and back on your feet. We'll put the wedding off until then.'

Kate saw the sacrifice that Lilly and Ned were making on her behalf, and felt humbled by it.

Kate would not have believed that a person could grow so large, if the evidence was not staring her in the face every day. John continued to tell her how much he loved her, but she often doubted his sincerity, citing that she looked something akin to a bloated cow. John would not be put off, however. As she wandered from her bedroom, making her way to the drawing room, she reflected on how blessed she really felt. That John should have accepted her, married her and loved her had been such a miracle in the midst of her previous distress, that she sometimes wondered if it were all a wonderful dream from which she would one day wake up. It was the sharp kicking of the baby that reminded her that her present status was no dream.

'Is Papa up to getting out of bed, today?' Kate asked Lilly as she came into the room.

'He was asleep when I checked on him for breakfast,' the girl answered. 'I haven't been back since. Would you like me to go now, or do you want to walk that far?'

'I need the exercise,' Kate gave a half smile. 'I will go.'

Lilly didn't bother to follow Kate, or to worry about her at all, and so the situation that developed didn't become apparent until some time later, when John returned from a call.

'Where's Kate?' he asked, seeing that she wasn't in her bed or the drawing room.

'I suppose she is with her father. She went to see him over an hour ago.'

John set out to find them both, but what he found was only his wife, bent in a state of stunned disbelief over the body of her departed father.

'He's gone!' Kate spoke the obvious, her voice amazingly calm. 'I came in to see if he wanted to get up, and he was asleep – or at least I thought he was asleep. Look.' She held up a book for John to see. 'It's the family Bible,' Kate informed him. 'He must have been updating the family tree in the front, see. He has written your name and the date of our first wedding in. And look, John. He has the birth date all ready filled in, except for the day. He was so certain it would come this month. I found the Bible open on the side table, the pen there ready to fill out the rest. He's gone, John. He won't ever write in the Bible again.'

John moved around the bed to his wife's side, and knelt down next to her. He expected her to crumble in sorrow, but she didn't. She seemed somehow strangely distant, as if the death of her father was not real. 'Let's go and have a cup of tea,' he suggested, not wanting to upset the deli- cately balanced atmosphere. 'Afterwards, I will ride over to the Hodges and have them come and sit with us for the rest of the day.'

'No, John!' Kate objected. 'Don't bother the Hodges. I will be all right. Perhaps I will go and lie down for a little while.'

John aided Kate to do as she requested. Once she was lying down, he sought out Lilly for counsel. 'She is taking his death rather too calmly, I think,' he offered, as if he wanted the housekeeper to contradict him. 'I would have expected her to be much more emotional.'

'I think it best we send word for Mrs Hodges to come. It's too far for the doctor to come to the Valley at such short notice. It's better if we have a midwife on hand, just in case.'

John nodded his agreement. 'I will need Hodges to help me prepare the body for the funeral, at any rate. Would you mind going for me, Lilly? I think I need to be close to Kate for the time being.'

The people at the manse moved through the mechanics of life, as if caught in a bad dream. Somehow, John thought it would have been better to have a lot of tears and to be done with it, but as it was, no one seemed quite ready to cry. Kate kept to her bed, and took a small amount of nourishment that Mrs Hodges insisted she eat. John kept to his expected schedule, and took the Sunday service at the church. When the sermon had ended, John shared the sad news with the congregation.

'I know that some of you may have felt disappointed with Reverend Winston in some ways, but I am convinced that many of you will be grieved, even as my wife and I are grieved, to know of his passing. The deception he played on you during a trying time in his life is something I know he regretted with all his heart. More than anything else, he desired to be forgiven. He loved you – the people of Green Valley – and I ask that you all would find it in your hearts to extend the forgiveness he so craved by attending his funeral service tomorrow. It will be held here, in this chapel, at two o'clock. Please use this opportunity to put away bitterness, and practice forgiveness. This is your last opportunity to pay your respects to a man, who in many ways, deserved your respect.'

John turned to exit from the pulpit, ready to make his way to the back of the church for the expected greetings, but was arrested by the sound of a voice he well knew; a voice that commanded a great degree of authority.

'That's a very pretty speech, Reverend,' Lady Vera spoke as one who didn't intend to be dismissed. 'But I, for one, forbid you to use this sacred hall for such a low purpose. Carlton Winston deceived us and used us all abominably. He cannot have thought it possible that he should waltz back here and just expect us all to forget the great wrong he did against the people who trusted him.'

'Lady Wallace, your attitude may have foundation in truth, but it is not the attitude of Christ. The Bible warns us of unforgiveness, and in this, you are at fault. I will hold the funeral service in this chapel, and the Reverend Winston will be buried in the churchyard.' A fire seemed to spark from John's eyes as he spoke. 'I am now offering each one of you an opportunity to fulfil your obligation to Christ himself. If you will not forgive others, how will you ever be forgiven?'

With these words said, John proceeded to march out of the building, not even pausing to greet his parishioners.

John was furious with himself, as much as anyone else. He didn't want to lose his temper, but Lady Wallace's persistent refusal to let go of her hurt, and her strong influence to keep others in the same pattern, seemed to make his blood boil. He had no doubt that his own position as parish minister was in jeopardy. In a bygone era that seemed ages past, but was in fact only a little over two years ago, he would have bowed to the manipulative pressure.

Lady Vera Wallace wielded her position, wealth and influence in a manner reminiscent of John's own mother. For years, John had yielded and complied, mostly with no harm caused, but as he thought on it now, he could see that his own character had suffered some terrible erosion. His failure to take a stand had caused a deficiency in his ability to hold to conviction. It wasn't that he needed to rebel against his mother's every wish, for that would have been defiance, and no better for his character; but it was now quite plain to him that he should have resisted on occasion, when his mother had demanded inappropriate action or unnecessary compliance. It was a matter of some concern now, that John was having to practice this form of conviction without confidence. He knew he could not obey Lady Wallace's decree. Carlton Winston's sin, while wrong and potentially damaging, had been repented of, and the consequences had been paid. John could not, and would not condone the patron Lady's bitter grudge. Even with the threat of dismissal, while facing the arrival of his first child to add to the difficulty, John declared to himself that he would not be influenced against his original decision.

Hodges caught up with John before he'd made it to the manse.

'I'm standin' with ye, son,' Hodges spoke in a low gruff voice. 'It may mean me job and home, but she is goin' too far this time.'

'It shouldn't have to be like this, Hodges,' John complained. 'Surely it must be my responsibility to teach proper theology. Have I failed to impart the truth on this issue? Has my own life shown a lack of forgiveness?'

'Stop this self-blame, boy. It can't be your responsibility if others choose a path of sin. I've heard ye speak the truth often enough.'

'Do you think that people will come to the funeral, then?' John sounded doubtful.

'People will be there, and that's for certain. But as to whether it will be the normal Sunday congregation or not will remain to be seen. I plan to spend the rest of today extendin' the news to the farmers. There is no doubt that they'll want a part in the service.'

A heated discussion had arisen in the kitchen of the manse between the resident midwife and the minister himself.

'Ye can't be allowin' yer wife to be goin' out in public while she is so heavy with child.' Mrs Hodges' voice was stern and unyielding. 'It's not decent, and folk would not expect her.'

'I understand the protocol, Mrs Hodges,' John sighed wearily, 'it's just that I'm convinced Kate needs to see her father laid to rest.'

'Phooey! What nonsense! No one would think any the less of her for not bein' at the graveside considerin' her condition.'

'It's not what people think that is my major concern,' John's voice rose in strength. 'It's what is best for Kate that concerns me.'

'What is best for a woman of her state is to be inside, restin' by the fire. She doesn't need all of this emotional upheaval right now.'

'I agree with you. The reverend's death could not have come at a worse time, but it has come, and I need to see that Kate deals with it properly.'

'What's there to deal with? The man has gone to his rest. Let it be at that.'

'Kate has not shed one tear yet. She is behaving as if it weren't real. Now I don't profess to know everything, but I have an instinct that this is not healthy for her. She needs to face reality for what it is. She needs to grieve, or she will carry the pain with her for the rest of her life. I have seen it happen before, and it can twist a person's mind, I tell you. The Bible tells us that there is a time to mourn as well as a time to rejoice. I want the mourning done and over with so that we can get on with the business of rejoicing. If she doesn't do it now, I fear that she will put her pain on our child. No, Mrs Hodges. I have made up my mind. Help her find something suitable to wear, if you will.'

'I'll not contend with ye further,' Mrs Hodges grumbled, 'but I ask ye make it clear that it was your decision, and that I don't support ye in it.'

'As you will.' John nodded his head, a grim expression firmly fixed. His fear for Kate's state of mind was very real. She seemed to exist in an ethereal realm, where the reality of her father's death did not penetrate. John knew that Mrs Hodges wanted to protect Kate from the grief, but it was a false hope. The hurt of losing one so close was too real, and Kate must feel it. John's one goal was to help her wash it from her soul with the expected tears and lament, for if she did not do at least this, the pain would certainly be carried deep in her soul, and a sadness would envelop her.

John remembered a cousin who had lost her first child, and had failed to mourn. He had witnessed firsthand the change from a vivacious and fun-loving girl, to a melancholy and forlorn woman. The process had only taken a matter of weeks, and nothing seemed able to resurrect the former character that had been so bright and full of life.

John dreaded the thought of losing the Kate he loved so dearly. He knew she must mourn, and he wanted to mourn with her; but he wanted to look forward to the time when mourning could be put aside, and they could move on in life.

CHAPTER 19

*T*echnically, it was still autumn, though winter hinted about its just being around the corner. One might have hoped that the day would be clear and still. Stable weather conditions would certainly have added to the ease of conducting a funeral service. But as it was, even the sky seemed intent to mourn. Mid-morning presented dull and overcast, a biting wind whipping around the corners of the church as if to announce the coming ceremony.

Just as John had decreed, Mrs Hodges had found a large black cape that was enough to cover Kate's whole dress, including the protruding stomach. She muttered and fussed under her breath, making it all too clear to everyone that she disapproved of Kate's going out of the manse.

By the time the hall clock had struck two, the entire family from the manse had taken up their respective positions in the church. Mrs Hodges sat one side of Kate, while Lilly took the other. Both women were dressed in the expected black. They waited quietly, not taking much notice of anything else, other than the wooden coffin that sat silently at the front of the church.

Kate was busily trying to fight an internal battle. She saw the coffin, and knew exactly what it meant; more importantly, who it contained. Her sensible mind consistently nudged her with the thoughts of what this service was supposed to represent, but Kate struggled to keep these thoughts at bay. Some stubborn part of her did not want to let go of her father. She simply did not want to acknowledge the facts as they stood before her. She had almost made up her mind to ask John to let her return home, and would have if he had not been drawn to the back of the church.

The look on Hodges face told John the story. 'Do you mean to tell me that no one has come to the service. Why, it's . . .'

'Hold on, there, son.' Hodges prevented him going further. 'There is a whole crowd of folks gathered in the yard outside, but none of them is willing to set foot inside this here building.'

'Why not? That's ridiculous, Hodges. If they're going to defy the Lady by coming, they may as well come right on in.'

'It's not the regular church folk who're here.' Hodges seemed uncomfortable imparting this information.

'Who, then?' John's tension was beginning to show.

'It's the farmers, lad. They want to pay their respects, but they don't feel they are dressed well enough to come inside.'

Uttering a mild exclamation of frustration, John pushed past the older gentleman, and forged his way outside. To his astonishment he saw nearly seventy people of all ages – men, women and children – milling about, quietly waiting for the time when the funeral procession would make its way to the churchyard. He saw one or two folk give a respectful nod of greeting as he came close. 'Sorry to hear of the reverend's passing,' someone muttered. 'He was a good man.'

'Yes! Yes he was,' John replied. 'Won't you good people come inside for the service?'

'Oh, no!' One man, who seemed to echo the feeling of the entire crowd, spoke. 'We could never degrade the holy place.'

'It is no more holy in there than it is out here,' John argued. 'Please don't stay outside, when I need your presence inside so badly.'

'Need us?' someone else asked. 'Why would you be needing us?'

'There's no one but the Hodges to support my wife in her time of loss. The rest of the congregation have elected to bow to Lady Wallace's pressure. If you do not come inside, I will have no one to address the eulogy to. For my wife's sake, please make your way inside, and take a seat.'

John did not wait to see if the crowd would respond. He turned back into the porch and made his way toward the front. The three women seated on the first pew did not turn around to see his progress, but remained in their hushed state of reverence, waiting for the service to begin. John took his place behind the pulpit, and opened his prayer book, preparing himself to begin, regardless of whether there was a congregation or not. He had taken that deep breath indicative of his being about to begin, when he was interrupted by first one, then another; one by one, the entire outside crowd coming in to become a part of the funeral service. He let out that deep breath as a sigh of relief. A lot of his tension drained away as he realised that there was support and encouragement for Kate, from the people she and her father had both loved.

Kate heard nothing of what her husband preached during the service. She had to shut out his words, because if she listened, it would have meant she would have had to acknowledge the facts, and that would have only led her down a path she didn't want to go. She could feel the emotion building in her; the deep down welling of pain and sorrow that she knew would burst forth in an eruption of tears and moaning. *I can't do that now*, she thought. *Not now. I have to hold myself together.*

And so she sat stiffly, apparently unmoved by the whole experience. It was enough to make even Mrs Hodges acknowledge that it was not a normal response under the current circumstances. By the time John had prayed the benediction and Hodges had arranged for several of Carlton's closer friends to bear the coffin on its way to the grave, Mrs Hodges began to admit that the young minister might have had grounds for his fears.

'It'd be quite all right for you to be cryin' at such a time as this, Katie,' she spoke kindly. 'No one would think any the worse of ye for it.'

'Yes! Thank you,' Kate answered quickly dismissing Mrs Hodges' words, and not allowing them to penetrate her thinking. She was still determined to capture every thought and keep them safely locked away. 'Perhaps it would be all right for me to go along home now,' she suggested hopefully.

Earlier in the day, Mrs Hodges would have been profoundly relieved to go along with such a suggestion, but now she had begun to subscribe to John's theory, and thought it was the best path to follow.

'Honey, I think it would be best we go along to the grave, and see your father properly laid to his rest.'

Kate continued to resist the knowledge that this was her last chance to acknowledge her father's life, determined to repress the emotion that such an acknowledgement would bring. Instead, she allowed herself to be steered after the funeral procession, outside and to the graveside. She stood stiffly, shivering in the icy wind, her ears unhearing and her eyes unseeing. A light misty rain had begun to fall, and though she did not recognise what was going on, John hurried the ceremonial words and prayers, before allowing the coffin to be lowered. Many of the folk gathered around allowed tears to escape; some even lost control of several sobs. It was a sombre scene, and one that spoke of the love the people had kept for their one-time minister and friend.

By the time most of the farming community had filed past the new minister and his wife, several had made comment that John could not help but overhear.

'Kate doesn't seem to have accepted what's going on. I hope she'll be all right, especially with the young one so close.'

A fear pierced through John's own consciousness. He had hoped that the funeral would have been enough to prompt the mourning process into action. When that had failed to draw so much as a tear, he hoped that the kind words of condolence offered by friends would be the trigger. But even though several women had broken down and cried as they spoke their words, Kate seemed unmoved by any of it.

With a heavy heart, John turned to the task of restoring Kate to the manse. Though he longed to say something, he couldn't think of anything that he'd not already said during the service and after. He wanted to comfort his wife in her loss, but she could not be comforted when she was not grieving. The whole situation troubled John greatly. The only consolation was that he now had an ally in the form of the midwife. At last, Mrs Hodges had begun to see the abnormality of the situation, and she vowed to him that she would do all in her power to set the circumstance to right.

The dinner hour came and went, though no one at the table seemed particularly inclined to eat. There was not much said, either, as each nursed their own thoughts. John felt that, while the day of the funeral should bring a melancholy atmosphere, the meal following should also be a time for talking out a lot of the depressed feelings. He was convinced that now was the time that should bring the bereaved family to offering a smile or two about the life of the departed loved one. But instead, it was all too obvious, no talk was going to be had, and no smile would be offered.

Kate sat with them, stiff and quiet, a glassy eyed look indicating that she was not really with them in her mind.

Mrs Hodges chafed and fretted inwardly. She now wondered what other plan the minister had to bring their girl back to the present. She worried over her food, and even her husband noticed her state of agitation, but wisely he held his tongue.

Finally, the dinner hour was over, and some sort of relief from the tension was gained when Kate excused herself and retired early to her bed. Though the remaining three wanted to discuss the many anxieties they all seemed to have, none of them dared, as if to speak any of their thoughts would have been an act of betrayal to the one who was absent from the discussion. Mrs Hodges saw to the cleaning up, and her husband excused himself for the night. They had decided that he would maintain his presence at the lodge, seeing to his tasks and chores as usual, while his wife remained at the manse in the capacity of midwife. It didn't take long before they all went to bed. There was not the opportunity to talk out their frustrations, and so sitting about with nothing to say only seemed to aggravate the situation.

'Thank you, Mrs Hodges,' John sighed before he left the drawing room. 'It's been a trying day, and I'm longing for some sleep.'

'I only hope you can get to sleep,' she replied, her discomfit apparent. 'Katie is getting close to term, and she must be restless from the baby, if not from anything else.'

It was an indirect reference to the older woman's concern, but John had nothing he could say in response or encouragement. He, himself, felt so discouraged that he wished that someone else had a word for him.

By the time John had turned out the lamp, and settled under the covers, he knew that sleep was determined to elude him. Kate appeared to be already heavy with sleep, and John was careful not to make any moves that might wake her. If it hadn't been for the fact that his wife was so pregnant, he would have, in frustration, woken her and demanded that they talk through the present emotional crisis. But as it was, he was afraid of her physical condition and so he held his frustrations to himself.

Hours of self-denial – wanting to yield to the impulse to toss and turn, yet resisting the urge – seemed endless to John. He was no nearer sleep and his intense mental search for an answer had been fruitless. He was almost at a point where he was ready to get back out of bed, so he could at least pace away his tension, when Kate stirred from her slumber. John waited, hopeful that he might at last have an opportunity to verbally express his anxieties, but any such opportunity was soon forgotten as a different situation quickly became evident.

Kate was not fully awake, but the dream she'd been having, of being in pain, was rapidly becoming a reality. As she drifted from that blurred realm of unconsciousness into awareness, she became all too sensible to the fact that the growing ache of her nightmare was not going to go away. She turned in the darkness, using all the effort of one who is heavily burdened, and reached out to her husband. Feeling that he was there beside her gave her a small measure of comfort in the face of the growing anxiety.

'Are you all right?' It was obvious that Kate was awake, and John used the question as a form of breaking his own state of restlessness.

'I'm not sure,' Kate answered, sounding as fearful as she felt.

'Why? What's the matter?' John was instantly alert.

'I think it's the baby,' she offered, 'but I'm scared, John. I don't think I can do this. Not now.'

Several comments flew through John's mind in response to Kate's words, but a few seconds consideration on each one caused him to abandon them as unsuitable. He had wanted to contradict her on the count of not being able to do this, but he pulled himself up on that, not knowing exactly what it was she had to do. Then he wanted to ask why not now? Did she think that just because her father had passed away that the whole world was going to stand still? But he soon saw that this was unnecessarily harsh. He wanted to tell her that there was nothing to be scared of, but then he considered how many reports he had heard of things going wrong during childbirth. It was with this thought that he began to allow a little fear of his own.

'I'll get Mrs Hodges,' were all the words he was eventually able to offer.

Somehow, now that John was leaving her, Kate was struck with dismay, desperately wanting him near. 'Please don't be long,' she ventured in a small voice. 'I need you.'

'I will only be a moment,' John answered in a practical tone, as he pulled on his trousers. The young husband had heard the pathetic tone in his wife's voice, and was moved by it. He was very quick in rousing the older woman from her sleep, and then returning, coming around to Kate's side of the bed. 'Mrs Hodges will make sure you're all right,' he tried to reassure her as he gathered her in a comforting embrace. 'It's been a trying day, and I'd feel happier if we were sure.' Kate clung to her husband, quite suddenly allowing her apprehension to be expressed in her grasp. John began to hope that perhaps she might be ready to break the emotional wall that she had so carefully put in place, and he waited for that possibility.

'It's been quite a long day, Kathryn,' he spoke in a low tone. 'I have been worried about you.' Once again he paused, holding her close, and stroking her hair with affection. John didn't quite know what he was expecting as a reward for his patience, but what came was certainly not what he had in mind. Quite without warning, Kate gave a sharp cry of pain. Mrs Hodges was hurried along as she heard it, and was only minutes before coming in to the main bedroom.

'It'll be time!' she muttered, tiredness still evident in her voice. 'There, there, child!' she clucked. 'We've a job to do now, and you'd best start concentrating on breathing rather than wasting good air on yellin'.'

John was horrified by the midwife's forthrightness, and he turned an almost angry expression her way. 'Kate is in pain, Mrs Hodges,' he blurted. 'Shouldn't you do something to help her?'

'Quite!' She didn't seem ruffled by his distress. 'The first thing we need to do is to get you out of here now. The birthin' room is no place for a man!' Mrs Hodges tone was firm and seemed to leave no room for argument.

'But . . .' John tried to voice his objection.

'There isn't any buts about it, Reverend. Your wife is about to give birth and we need our privacy. Go along and fetch my man, if you will. He'll sit with you a while, and perhaps he can inform you of a husband's place.'

Kate looked wild eyed at the prospect of allowing John to go, but Mrs Hodges had firm control of the situation, and set right about putting her mind at ease. 'Now Katie,' she began in a no nonsense manner, 'you know as well as I do that this is woman's work. The sooner you let your man go, the sooner we can get on with our job.'

If it weren't for another spasm of pain, Kate might not have released her hold on her husband, but this was the very opportunity that the older woman needed to accomplish her first goal.

'Come along, Reverend.' She took strong hold of his arm and ushered him toward the door, all the time ignoring his objections. 'She'll be just fine. You go off and find Hodges, and the two of you can talk about the weather.'

John backed reluctantly from the room, his eyes telling him that Kate was not at all fine, as he saw her gripped with agony. But there was no going back. Mrs Hodges was quick to shut the bedroom door, almost in his frantic face.

'Dear God, let her be all right!' John uttered the prayer in desperation before setting out to waken the gatekeeper from his sleep.

CHAPTER 20

Hodges had not seemed overly concerned when John had come banging on his front door in the early hours of the morning. 'All right! All right!' he muttered crossly. 'Who's been murdered?' But when he saw the young minister's excited expression, he knew at once that no soul had been brought to its end at all. 'I take it your wife's time has come?' Hodges guessed correctly.

'Hurry up, Hodges,' John spoke his impatience. 'We are wasting precious minutes here.'

'Won't be any use you scurryin' back there like a breathless rabbit. They won't let you in, and there ain't nothin' you can do to help. You may as well calm down, take a few deep breaths, and we will travel back to the manse at a decent pace, and without riskin' our health to accidents.'

'But, Hodges . . .' John attempted to argue but was instantly cut off by the older man's holding up his hand in authority.

'Breathe deeply, son. It's going to be a long night, and I'll not be able to put up with all your craziness the whole time. Take a grip of yourself, lad, or I'll just go right back inside, and go back to me warm bed.'

John was stunned and angered by the threat, but obeyed anyway, taking the opportunity to actually catch his breath. That part of the advice, at least, he was willing to follow. But his frustration didn't lessen, and in fact only increased, as Hodges pottered around his home, taking his own sweet time to get ready to go. Eventually, John abandoned his temporary self-control.

'I don't know how you can be so calm at a time like this!' he all but accused.

'A time like what?' Hodges asked.

'Kate could be dying back there, and you don't seem to care about that at all.'

'Did my wife tell you she was dying?' Hodges asked the question seriously, hoping that he hadn't underestimated the situation. 'Has she indicated any reason for alarm?'

John thought about the last words he'd exchanged with the midwife before leaving, and gradually he had to admit that she had not expressed any concern at all. But the evidence his own mind had gathered still seemed enough reason to be anxious.

Apparently the older gentleman must have thought better of delaying and decided to comply with John's need to hurry. 'Come along, then,' he finally announced, picking up his jacket and shrugging into it. John expelled his relief in a deep sigh, and didn't need to be invited twice to follow Hodges' lead. The pair travelled in silence for the first five minutes, though John was too involved with his own tumultuous thoughts to notice.

'It'll be all right, you know,' Hodges eventually broke into the sound pattern of the horse's feet rhythmically plodding along. 'These things usually work out just fine.'

'Usually?' John asked alert at once. 'I don't know if usually is enough.'

'You shouldn't borrow trouble,' Hodges continued in his calm reassurance. 'I don't know what your past experience has been in these sorts of circumstances, but it would be better to hope for the best.'

'I've just heard too many instances where things have gone wrong.' John seemed sorry that he couldn't accept

Hodges good advice. 'Too many reports of, you know, the mother not making it.'

'That'll be enough of that, son. Our Katie will make it just fine. You just turn your thoughts to prayer, and between my wife and God there should be a new member to the manse by tomorrow night.'

John didn't want to contradict his companion. He really wanted to accept the hope that was offered, and so he withheld any more attempts at reciting the possible complications.

Kate's body had well established the rhythm of painful contractions in its effort to deliver the child she carried. But Kate was not cooperating with the natural course of events. Though she was well aware of what was actually happening, her mind had taken up the belated cause of grieving. All she could think of was the sight of her father's coffin being lowered into the ground, and she began to moan as much with the emotional pain of loss as with the physical pain of contraction. The two situations – the death of her father and the birth of her child – merged into the one agonising experience. Mrs Hodges watched the events unfold before her eyes with concern. She recognised the physical symptoms as that of a woman in labour, and would not have begrudged the emotional display except that it was fast revealing a depth of despair beyond what could be expected in childbirth. 'Hush, child,' she soothed. 'You shouldn't be wastin' all your energy on cryin' now. There's too much work to be done.'

As if in response to her direction, Kate went into a physical paroxysm, clenching her fists and holding her breath. 'Relax, relax,' Mrs Hodges found herself coaching, not happy to see Kate give in so readily to the torturous contractions. 'You should concentrate on trying to keep even breath.'

But all of the midwife's good advice was wasted on a mind caught up with grief. Kate's thoughts were quite suddenly full of regret, even tormenting her with thoughts of having failed to do something properly. Once the pain had subsided, Kate took up the emotional storm in a form of a panicked cry. 'I can't go on,' she cried, 'it hurts too much. I didn't want him to go.'

'He'll be back soon,' Mrs Hodges tried to comfort. 'Don't worry yourself, Katie. He won't be long away.'

'Don't!' Kate was almost fierce in her denial. 'I know he's gone. I was at the graveside with you, remember.' Each word spoken came out over a convulsive sob. 'I didn't ever think he would really die, but he has. I was there!'

Mrs Hodges realised her mistake in thinking that Kate was upset over her husband's absence. On the one hand she felt it good to know that Kate had at last accepted that her father had gone, but on the other, she was troubled. She knew how much mental, emotional and physical energy grieving could sap from a normal healthy individual, but to begin such a process in the midst of labour was reason for concern. She watched the pattern form and become regular with her patient. Each contraction brought with it the tension and cry of one unable to cope, and set into a routine coming at intervals of only two or three minutes. And following the easing of the pain, Kate began to beg for a reprieve in an almost hysterical manner. 'Please, Mrs Hodges,' she pleaded, 'can't you make this pain stop? I'm not ready to do this now. Papa has only just been buried.'

But before Mrs Hodges could respond, Kate was taken in the grips of yet another contraction. 'Relax, Katie!' the midwife barked. 'Breathe, child, for goodness sake. Concentrate on breathing.'

'I want to say goodbye to my Papa,' were all the words that Kate could manage to express back.

Several hours passed with Mrs Hodges trying every way she knew how to snap Kate's mind to reason. But try as she might, she was unsuccessful in making the younger woman understand that she should put all of her energy into concentrating on delivering her baby. She simply couldn't get Kate to cooperate in a way that may have aided the birth of the child.

John had been back in the manse for nearly an hour, hearing the emotional storm that was in action behind the closed door. He looked desperately to his counsellor for permission to break the door down.

'T'won't do you no good blunderin' in there,' Hodges recited calmly, again and again. 'There ain't nothin' you or I can do to help. It's women's work, and they have managed perfectly well without us for years. Our job is to wait and to pray.'

'I can't pray!' John was almost violent in his denial.

'You're the minister, son,' Hodges reminded gently.

'It doesn't make any difference who I am,' John argued. 'How can any man think, let alone pray, when his wife is in agony like that?'

Hodges didn't bother to try and find some theological answer, as he knew that any such exertion on his part would be wasted on a mind fevered with anxiety.

The nervous tension stretched out painfully for another half hour before it was broken by Mrs Hodges coming into the kitchen from the bedroom.

'Well?' John leapt up from his seat like a tightly coiled spring, instantly noting the look of worry that decorated the nurse's face. 'Is she . . . she's not . . .'

'I'll need your help, Reverend,' Mrs Hodges blurted straight out.

'Help? How?' Hodges facial expression mirrored the minister's question.

'Katie's finally taken to her grieving, but it's the worst time. She can't seem to think of anything but the funeral and her father being gone. I can't seem to make her understand that the baby is coming, and she needs to work at it.'

'Won't the baby just come on its own?' John displayed his ignorance by the question.

'Normally, I suppose it probably would, but . . .'

'But what?' John was full of nervous energy and aggression.

'The baby is not turned right. Kate is going to have to pour all of her energy into this, or we might . . .'

'Might what?' Fear coursed through John as he understood what the midwife was getting at. 'Could we lose them?'

'Let's just get back to her, and your job will be to get her mind properly focused. And Hodges, you'd better pray, and pray hard.'

John walked into his bedroom as one walking on hallowed ground. This was the birthing room – a place forbidden to all men.

'Talk to her,' Mrs Hodges whispered loudly to him. 'Make her understand.'

John was overwhelmed by the atmosphere and the sight that greeted him. He saw his beautiful wife lying against the propped up pillows, her expression showing exhaustion; her eyes swollen and red from crying; her hair loose and matted; her nightclothes damp with perspiration.

'Kathryn!' He tested the silence. 'It's me. John.' She opened her eyes in response, but before the light of recognition was lit, another contraction seized her, and she was once again in the grips of severe pain.

'Shouldn't we do something?' John's tone betrayed his panic. 'Look at her, she's dying.' He may have spoken more, but a murderous glance from Mrs Hodges silenced him.

'It's normal,' she hissed under her breath. 'What we have to do is to make her cooperate with the pain, instead of fighting it. She needs to start pushing the baby out. You need to make her understand what her job is.'

Mrs Hodges pushed John forward toward the chair next to the bed. 'I don't know how or what to do,' John confessed. 'What am I supposed to say?'

'I don't know, Reverend, but you'd better think of something soon, because her life depends on it. Do you understand?'

John was shocked into compliance by the seriousness of the charge, and he turned his attention to his wife, now emerging from the painful spasm.

'John,' she reached out to him. 'Oh, John. How can I go on now? It hurts too much.'

'You have to work hard, Kate, and then the pain will go away.' He made a halting attempt to explain, taking her hand to begin to comfort her.

'But I hoped Papa would live to see his grandchild. I didn't want him to go suddenly like that.'

'It's right for you to feel sad, Kate. It hurts me too. I had hoped that Carlton would see our baby.' He didn't go on as Kate dissolved into a further mess of tears, which quickly turned to another contraction. 'Don't leave me, John!' she screamed. 'Hold me.'

John had nothing left to do but comply, but his own heart hammered with fear at the intensity of it all. Eventually the pain subsided.

'I know the baby's coming,' Kate told her husband.

'Yes, Kate.' John tried to hide his impatience. 'Mrs Hodges says that you have got to concentrate and work hard.'

'I don't think I can.' Kate's tone was all resignation and defeat. 'I don't feel as if I can go on.'

'You must!' John's voice rose in passion. 'Kate, I need you. You can't give up on me.'

'But it's too hard, now. I feel so empty and lost.'

'I know, love,' John acknowledged her feelings. 'I know it hurts to lose someone so close, but you must see that your father would want his grandson born alive. Carlton would want him to know and love his mother. You've got to work at it, Kate. For your father's sake. So we can write the date and name in your father's family Bible.'

John was forced to cease his narrative during another interruption, but he began to feel as if Kate had at least begun to see reason.

'It'll be time for her to begin to push,' Mrs Hodges stated plainly. 'Kate, do you think you can manage that?'

'I don't know if I can.' She sounded uncertain.

'This is the grandchild that your father wanted so much, Kate. Let's work for that. You can do it.' John felt as if he had a point of leverage now.

During the next half hour, Kate began to cooperate and work hard, just as the midwife suggested. John watched Mrs Hodges' face anxiously, looking for signs of promise.

'I think we can make it from here,' the older woman suddenly announced out of the blue. 'We're beginning to make ground. You can take your proper place out in the kitchen until it's all over.'

Torn with feelings of ambivalence – half wanting to stay, half wanting to leave the tension of it all – John began to obey the orders given, but was soon arrested in his attempt to leave.

'No! No!' Kate objected. 'I can't do this alone. Don't leave me, John. Please.' There was definite panic in her tone, and John turned questioning eyes to Mrs Hodges for direction.

'It's no place for a man, Katie,' the older woman recited. 'We'd be better off on our own now.' But Kate was not listening to the logic of tradition. All she could understand was her fear of being left alone.

'I need him here,' she argued tearfully. 'Please, don't make him go.'

Because she could see their hard gained advantage slipping from their grasp, Mrs Hodges relented. 'There, there, child. He can stay if you want.' John returned to his position by the bedside, but he heard the muttered comments the older woman turned his way.

'I've never heard of such a thing in all my born days. Don't you let it be known that I let a man in the birthin' room. It's not right, and if it weren't for . . .'

'It's all right, Mrs Hodges,' John reassured. 'I won't breathe a word of it.'

It was an hour and a half, and much anxiety later, that John completely forgot his promise to the ruffled midwife as he burst from the bedroom and announced to Hodges:

'It's a girl, Hodges. All this time we thought it would be a boy, and it's a girl, and I saw it all!'

As the words tumbled from his lips he began to realise just what it was he had seen, and he suddenly felt very weak at the knees. 'Your wife is right,' he began. 'The birthing room is no place for a man.'

CHAPTER 21

Mixed feelings fought for attention at the manse during the following days. It was traditional for the family of the deceased to endure a period of mourning, complete with the wearing of black; but John was struggling to maintain the sombre exterior expected. He had been firsthand witness to one of life's brilliant moments. He had been witness to the miracle of childbirth, a privilege, he realised, not common for one of his sex.

But even if he hadn't been with his wife for the whole rewarding ordeal, he could not squash the feelings of pride that threatened to reduce him to a mass of cotton wool every time he thought of his new daughter. Still, he carefully tried to observe protocol, thanking his parishioners for the rather subdued congratulations, 'considering the circumstances'. He acknowledged, along with his many visitors, that it was a shame that young Kate had the trial of grief at a time when they both should have felt the greatest joy. But John didn't pass these comments along to his wife.

Mrs Hodges had prescribed peace and quiet for the young mother, and had warned visitors away at this early stage. And so Kate had plenty of time to reflect on the happenings of the past few days. Her clarity of thought had returned following the delivery, and she at last began to take account of her father's passing, the funeral, and then the bittersweet agony of labour. It only took several days for Kate to complete the introspection, and by the time those days had passed, she emerged from her natural depression into the blossoming joys of motherhood. It was as if the pain of loss and the pain of childbirth had been packaged together, and now all that was left was the joy of welcoming a new life into the world.

'I really don't know what we should call her,' John spoke quietly, three days later. He was holding the baby, and totally captured by her perfectly formed baby face and features. 'I had set in my mind that we would call our boy Carlton Winston Laslett, after your father. But it would seem that God had other ideas. He has sent us a darling girl instead.' Kate simply nodded her agreement, not yet ready to burst forth in conversation. 'It was very remiss of me not to have planned for such an outcome,' John murmured as an afterthought.

The young couple continued in the dreamlike atmosphere for a while longer, neither one wanting to waste words on thoughtless chatter. Eventually, John took up the thought again. 'Do you have any ideas, Kate?' he asked. 'We can't keep calling her "the baby". Perhaps we should name her after you.'

Kate gave a gentle smile, shaking her head in the process. 'Would you mind, John, if we named her for my mother?'

'Your mother?' John was surprised by the suggestion, knowing how Lizzie Winston had deserted her baby daughter and husband for another man. Perhaps he felt a small wave of fear at the association, and the remote possibility that such an affair might find a repeat in history.

'I think it's time that I took positive action where my mother is concerned,' Kate went on talking, her strength of tone increasing with obvious conviction. 'I never knew her, yet all the years that Papa was my only parent, he never once taught me to hate her. He always loved her, and his forgiving attitude was really the only example I ever saw of how I should treat her memory. Somehow, I know that he grieved over the fact that I never had a mother – that his Katie and his Lizzie never knew each other, and never shared a mother daughter relationship. Perhaps, in honour of his memory, his Katie and his Elizabeth can now be mother and daughter together. I would like to call her Elizabeth – if that's all right with you.'

John nodded silently, chasing away the stupid fear that had threatened his security.

'And if you have no other preference, I would like to honour your sister by giving the second name of Sandra. Elizabeth Sandra Laslett. Do you like that?'

'I like it very much,' John smiled, 'and Aunt Sandra will be ecstatic. I wouldn't be surprised if she takes the trouble to travel out here for the christening.'

'Do you think we will still be here, in the manse, by the time we hold the christening?' Kate asked.

'Why wouldn't we still be here?' John sounded puzzled.

'You defied Lady Wallace by holding Papa's funeral in the church. I might not have shown it on the day, but I noticed who it was that turned up to the service. Now, when I think on it, I can guess what sort of things she must have said to make the normal congregation stay away.'

'She may have laid down the law, Kate, but she must know that her attitude is wrong. I don't believe that even Lady Wallace could be that unfair. But even if she were to act against us, I am not afraid of the future. Somehow, I know that God has brought us together as a team for a purpose. We work well together, Kate, and he will see to it that we have an opportunity to work for his purpose.'

'At the moment,' Kate confessed, 'I'm quite willing to rest in your confidence, especially when my own is so weak. I trust you, John, whatever the outcome.'

John began to regain his confidence now that Kate had returned to rational thought and logic. He had dreaded the thought that she might never recover her former personality, and that the family would be reduced to one who lived under a cloud of suppressed grief. But as it was, Kate was gaining strength and spirit every day. Mrs Hodges began to hum her little tunes that indicated that all was well with the world. Even though, strictly speaking, the manse should still have exhibited some sign of mourning, the majority of parishioners forgave them, choosing instead to join in the hesitant attempt at joy.

Elizabeth grew happily, completely unaware that she had come into the world only days following the exit of her grandfather from it. As days turned into weeks, and then into months, the child brought just the right mix of delight and satisfaction. Her aunt, just as John had predicted, had written several communiqués asking if a christening date had been set yet. She openly declared her intention to attend, and even hinted that John's mother, Mrs Laslett, might be induced to make the arduous journey to the Valley.

But for all of the positives, one unhappy fact persisted in clouding the future. John had continued to deliver his weekly sermons in the church, but the congregation had dwindled greatly in size. As was his duty and calling, John rode from home to home, inquiring after the health and welfare of each parishioner. But to his distress, the ones whom he was particularly concerned for, the ones who had been absent from Sunday services for so long, were the very ones who turned his visits away at the door. John confessed to his wife his feelings.

'I know that they are acting out of loyalty to Lady Wallace,' he tried to excuse their behaviour, 'but it still hurts every time I'm refused admittance.'

Kate wanted so much to protect John from the pain of rejection, but there was little she or anyone else could do. 'Lady Wallace has not returned to service, either,' Kate observed. 'Have you tried to get an audience with her?'

'I have tried and tried. Even Hodges is reluctant to ask on my behalf. She is truly angry with me for defying her, especially in public.'

'But if she is so angry, why hasn't she given us notice? She had no scruples when it came to evicting my father from his position.'

'Kate,' John sighed. 'Please don't take this the wrong way, but . . .'

'But what?' Kate sounded a little defensive.

'When your father's lie was discovered, Lady Vera felt she had perfect right to evict him because of his moral failure. However, in this instance, I believe she knows that I am right in taking a stand on forgiveness. She could not back up another such bold move with any biblical authority because she knows that she should have forgiven your father. All that is left to her, now that her authority is weakened, is her power to manipulate. I suppose, if she thinks she can keep the parish under her control, and out of the church, for long enough, she will have some sort of excuse to get rid of us. She cannot maintain a minister that the people do not support.'

'But there are many people who support you,' Kate argued fiercely. 'What about all of those friends who came to Papa's funeral?'

'Good people!' John agreed. 'The trouble is that they still won't come and join with us in Sunday services. They still hold to this sense of class – of knowing their place and sticking to it. I'm afraid we are going to have to wait until this generation dies out before we will be able to change that pattern of thinking.'

Kate shook her head in frustration. 'How long are we going to be able to go on like this?' she asked. 'How long will it be before we are literally voted out of Green Valley?'

'Unless there is a direct intervention of the Lord – a miracle – I'm afraid we won't be here much longer.'

'But where will we go?' Kate's fear was evident in her tone.

'At this stage, my dear, I am still believing for that miracle. I'm not so sure that our work here in Green Valley is finished yet.'

Things continued on in the same worrying pattern for the next few weeks. Kate tried not to become anxious about it, and was greatly aided by the knowledge that her sister-in-law and her mother-in-law intended to pay a visit to the new grandchild. John agreed that they should plan the christening for the time when his family would arrive, and so Kate had her mind and hands full preparing for the forthcoming visit.

Lilly had long since left her position as housekeeper, having finally felt free to marry her young man. Kate had to admit that having another pair of hands in the house was not only a help but a blessing. Mrs Hodges had also returned to her own home, though making it her business to call by on frequent occasion. Still, there was a hole left in their absence, and it didn't take John long to talk Kate into employing another girl as a housekeeper. The Smyths' second daughter took the role and worked efficiently at it. Kate was doubly blessed, knowing that not only were her needs met, but that Emily Smyth was taking home much needed cash to help feed her numerous siblings.

As the week of the christening approached, Kate's anticipation rose to fever pitch. She looked forward with excitement to seeing Sandra again. After all, it was Sandra who had been so instrumental in making the pretend marriage into a real one. Kate also had mixed feelings about seeing her mother-in-law again. Mrs Laslett had received her with a distant sort of acceptance on their one and only meeting. Kate truly hoped that she would be proud of her son and his family.

Friday dawned bright, showing hopeful signs of the arrival of spring, and with it the promise of the arrival of the visitors from Melbourne. John went with Hodges to Brinsford to meet the train. As it was, Hodges took the carriage without Lady Wallace's knowledge. It had gotten that way that Hodges dared not mention anything about the people in the manse for fear of her reaction. He continued to serve the young family, despite this, and waited, even as John and Kate waited, for the day when he would be served notice of dismissal. But no notice had eventuated so far, and so the friends continued on in the hope that a miracle might yet change the difficult tension of the situation.

Kate could not contain her gush of emotion when she saw Sandra approach. The two fell upon one another in hugs and tears, forsaking all appearance of etiquette. John's mother, however, sniffed her disapproval, and held any feeling she might have had behind her schooled features.

'I'm so glad you have made the journey to be with us,' Kate expressed her welcome with energy. 'It is wonderful to see you again after all this time.'

'Thank you,' Mrs Laslett answered, somewhat stiffly. 'I must say I am somewhat shocked to see how small the manse is. You know, John, you could have had much larger accommodations had you taken a position in the city. I'm sure I don't know why you were so insistent that you come out all this way to find a place.'

'This place is quite dear to me, Mother,' John spoke in quiet confidence. 'If I had never come to Green Valley, then I would never have met my darling wife, I would not have married, and you would not have a precious granddaughter.'

'You see,' Sandra chimed in cheerily, 'there is a grand side to every tale. Now where is this new niece of mine? I have been absolutely dying to see her.'

From that moment on, Mrs Laslett seemed to have nothing left to say. John had taken a firm stand, even if it was quietly. Sandra allowed her vivacious personality to fill the manse with life and merriment. Kate relaxed immediately and began to enjoy the relationship for what it was. Elizabeth's grandmother was cool and distant, and held the baby as affectionately as a statue of Queen Victoria might. Kate felt somewhat sorry for her mother-in-law for she began to see that she had shut away the true feelings of life behind a wall of proper behaviour and protocol. She felt sorry that their relationship with Lady Wallace was so strained, as she felt that Mrs Laslett would have gotten on very well with the lady from the house.

John felt a little overwhelmed by the invasion of female presence in his home; still he thanked the Lord that his mother had made the effort, even if she exhibited her dis-approval at every turn. John was glad to acknowledge that he was now at a place where he felt secure with or without his mother's approval. He didn't begrudge his mother her opinions, but he didn't allow their negativity to encroach on his own sense of purpose and destiny. He was truly pleased that he had grown this far. Now, as he prepared for the christening service, he wondered if he would ever restore a level of relationship with Lady Wallace. He recognised her attempt to manipulate him into humility, and he also reaffirmed in his own mind, his intention to maintain his conviction. He had sent the entire parish handwritten invitations to attend the christening, and now as he pondered, he wondered just how many of the former congregation would attend.

It was not until Sunday that John found out the answer. Mr and Mrs Hodges were dressed in their Sunday best, wearing the proud smiles of surrogate grandparents. John's mother and sister occupied one of the front pews, and it was painful for John to see his mother's obvious recognition that there were few people to celebrate the christening. Lilly came alone, dressed in the dress she had worn for Reverend Winston's funeral. John knew that other friends milled about the outside of the church, and he wondered if he should go to them and plead, as he had done on the day of the funeral. But he eventually elected to proceed with the handful inside. He didn't think it would be appropriate to beg those outside to come in. If they had felt comfortable to come in, they would have by now, he reasoned.

Pushing aside his regret, and the knowledge of what his mother's criticism must be at the finish, John began the service, and preached of the love the Heavenly Father has for children. He spoke of the purpose that every child has in God, and the hope he had, as the earthly father, that this purpose would be fulfilled. Finally he performed the traditional ceremony of sprinkling the infant's head with water, praying a blessing on the child as he did so.

Kate felt proud of her husband, despite the coldness she sensed from her mother-in-law. She knew him to be a man who would do what was right, no matter the opposition, no matter the lack of support. John would stand for righteousness, and Kate felt the security of this. Still she allowed several small tears to escape the corner of her eyes. Despite her love for him, she still felt his pain at so obvious a rejection. She wished with all her heart that she could make such a pain go away.

As John dismissed the tiny congregation, Kate longed to be able to stay with him, to hold him in her embrace and communicate all of her love and support, but ceremony dictated otherwise. At least, she thought, his mother would be obliged to withhold her criticism until they were safely back in the manse. Kate filed past her minister husband, giving him a shy smile for courage.

John turned back to the altar. He could have followed the family into the courtyard, but he wanted a few moments to reflect. He used several domestic details as an excuse to linger. It was as he was deep in thought, and in the process of folding away an altar cloth, that he was disturbed by someone returning into the sanctuary. John looked up, half expecting to see his wife breaking tradition to come in search of him. But instead he saw Lady Wallace, wearing an expression he could not read.

'I suppose you have reached your final decision, then?' John guessed.

'Yes, I have.' Despite the strange facial cast, Lady Wallace retained all authority in her tone.

'How long do we have before you want us out?' John's tone betrayed some defeat.

'Out?' Lady Wallace sounded surprised.

'You cannot mean to keep a minister who has so clearly lost public support?'

'I see you have read my game quite well,' Lady Wallace spoke as a commendation. 'It is true. I have seen to it that the people withdraw their support of you. It was the only way, really, that I could with good conscience dismiss you.' John made no comment, only waited. 'But conscience is something that you have taught well, Reverend. The closer I came to succeeding in my goal, the worse my conscience became. You needn't look so surprised, young man,' she snapped. 'I do believe in all that doctrine you preach. I just don't like to lose control of any situation. Control is something I have been brought up with, you realise. People feel more secure if their leader is in control of every situation.'

John opened his mouth to object, but was cut off.

'You needn't start with any new sermons, sir. I am perfectly aware that I have been wrong in my treatment of you.' She paused to see if he was accepting her attempt at apology. 'All right,' she conceded, 'I have wronged your wife and her father too. I had no right to judge Kate in the way I did. And I should have forgiven Carlton much sooner. Are you happy, Reverend? You have reduced me to your own social equal. I have admitted fault, and now ask you forgive me my sins.'

John couldn't help but smile. Even in her vulnerability, Lady Wallace still had to be lady of the manor.

'I will forgive you on one condition,' John spoke lightly.

'Condition? Forgiveness has conditions?'

'You're right,' John relented. 'Then I will just make it an open invitation. I would be honoured, Lady Wallace, if you would join with my family in the celebration of my daughter's christening.'

'Yes, I was rather put out that I hadn't been invited before,' the Lady complained as she walked with the minister out of the church. 'I do like to be present at such important occasions, you know.'

Later, when all the family had settled for the night, and the joy of celebration had calmed down, John spoke with Kate. 'This morning, I had almost given up on that miracle,' he confessed.

'But oh, how good it feels to be sure of your direction again.' Kate spoke with enthusiasm. 'There is such joy in forgiveness, John, isn't there?'

'It's always been the way of it,' John acknowledged, as he settled down into his bed, and took his wife into his embrace. 'Forgiveness has served us well.'

Coming soon . . .

GREEN VALLEY

The second novel in the
Heart of Green Valley
Series

By Meredith Resce

Emily Wallace has been given a choice. Either she marries the elderly widower, as her father has asked, or she will be sent to live with her aunt. Even with the tales of wild animals and convicts, Emily chooses to sail to Australia. She simply cannot marry the cruel and arrogant Lord.

Colin Shore has never met anyone so beautiful before. The moment he first saw Lady Emily Wallace at the dock he fell in love with her. But he would never presume that she would be part of his life. After all, she was a Lady and he was only a farmer.